S0-AKN-175

YEAR	NAME OF STUDENT
1982-83	Bettina Bachus
1983-1984	Jerry Long
'83-'84	Brian Mill

EXCELLENT

Spelling: WORDS and SKILLS

Authors

Ronald L. Cramer
W. Dorsey Hammond
Lida F. Lim
John Prejza, Jr.
DeWayne Triplett

Reader Consultants

Rebecca Marie Fernandez
Raymond Sunbury

Scott, Foresman and Company
Editorial Offices: Glenview, Illinois

Regional Sales Offices: Palo Alto, California •
Tucker, Georgia • Glenview, Illinois •
Oakland, New Jersey • Dallas, Texas

Here are some steps to help you study your words.

Before you write each word:
> Look at the word.
> Look at the letters.
> Say the word.
> Listen to the sounds.

When you write each word:
> Copy the word from your list.
> Remember how the word is spelled and
> > write it.

After you write each word:
> Check the word with your list.
> Do you see any mistakes?
> Notice where the mistakes are and
> > begin the steps again.

Each regular lesson in this book has four parts:
Part A gives the word list.
Part B is a practice page.
Part C includes proofreading, handwriting, and
dictionary work.
Part D has extra lists of words you can learn.

Every sixth lesson is a review lesson. After taking a
test at the end of each regular lesson, choose two list
words that you misspelled or found most troublesome. Record
these personal list words in the indicated place in the
review lesson.

You will see symbols like /a/ in lessons in this book.
These symbols stand for sounds. For example, /a/
stands for the sound of the letter **a** in *cat*.

ISBN 0-673-12714-1

Copyright © 1978
Scott, Foresman and Company, Glenview, Illinois.
All Rights Reserved.
Printed in the United States of America.

4 5 6 7 8 9 10 11 12 13 14 15 16 17 18 19 20 21 22 23 24 25 –RRC– 88 87 86 85 84 83 82 81 80 79

CONTENTS

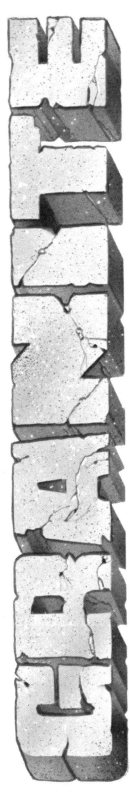

ADAPT YOUR THINKING

Part A

Say the words in the list below. Write the words.

1. adopt
2. adapt
3. allude
4. elude
5. choose
6. chose
7. loose
8. lose
9. trail
10. trial
11. granite
12. granted
13. implied
14. inferred
15. preceding
16. proceeding
17. quit
18. quite
19. affect *
20. effect *

Notice that these list words are arranged in pairs. The words in each pair are easily confused because their spellings are similar. However, their meanings are <u>not</u> similar. You will learn the difference between the easily confused words as you complete this lesson.

The first two list words are spelled similarly.

- Write the first list word. This word means "take or use as one's own choice."
- Change the **o** in the word you have just written to an **a** and write the new word that is formed. This word means "adjust; make fit or suitable."

✱Wild Words   *Effect* and *affect* are often confused in writing. Generally, *affect* is used only as a verb and *effect* is most commonly used as a noun.

Test Score: _____ —20   **4**   *Part A Score:* _____ —2

Part B

hat, āge, fär;
let, ēqual, tėrm;
it, īce; hot, ōpen, ôrder;
oil, out; cup, pùt, rüle;
ch, child; ng, long; sh, she;
th, thin; ŦH, then;
zh, measure;

ə represents *a* in about,
e in taken, *i* in pencil,
o in lemon, *u* in circus.

1. For each sentence below write the list word given in pronunciation symbols. Use the glossary if you need additional help.

  a. Jim tripped on his (lüs) shoelace.
  b. We were afraid our team would (lüz) the game.
  c. We (chōz) the path that led through the woods.
  d. The defendant had to (chüz) a lawyer.
  e. The judge postponed the (trī′əl) for a month.
  f. We left the (trāl) and started overland.
  g. Marcella is (kwīt) worried about her grades.
  h. Yesterday, Rory (kwit) her job.
  i. The governor (grant′əd) him a pardon.
  j. The large (gran′it) building was beautiful.
  k. His red face (im plīd′) that he was embarrassed.
  l. We (in fėrd′) from her yawn that she was tired.
  m. The drug will not (ə fekt′) your eyesight.
  n. Do you know the (ə fekt′) of this drug?
  o. We had to (ə dapt′) the material to our plans.
  p. Our neighbors want to (ə dopt′) a child.
  q. They are (prə sē′ding) with the case.
  r. The (prē sē′ding) announcement was prerecorded.
  s. The fox tried to (i lüd′) the bloodhounds.
  t. I did not (ə lüd′) to your nasty remark.

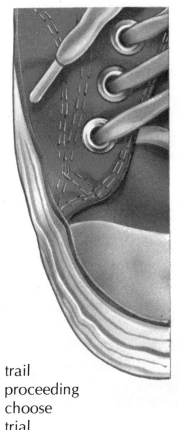

2. If you have to divide a word in which two vowel letters appear together, remember that a syllable break occurs between the vowels if each one is sounded (as in **fu-el**). But if the vowels form only one sound, as in *view,* a break does not occur between them. Pronounce the words at the right aloud; then write the word in which the vowel letters have two distinct sounds and form two syllables.

trail
proceeding
choose
trial
loose

WHAT'S THE BIG IDEA?

If you know how the spellings and meanings differ in these pairs of words, you can use the words correctly.

PROOFREADING

Correct spacing between words and sentences is important in good handwriting. Rewrite the following sentences, spelling correctly each misspelled word and remembering that correct spacing does make a difference.

1. *The trail was preceding slowly when the judge granite a recess.*

2. *The next day, however, he choose not to elude to this problem.*

Rewrite this paragraph, correcting the spelling errors and using correct spacing between words and sentences.

3. *The granted rock marked the end of the trial we choose. Because the trail was so well marked, we did not loose our way. Surprisingly, no one wanted to quite.*

1. Write the list word that rhymes with each word below.

planet	hit	planted	kite
noose	style	cruise	pale

2. Make couplets with the pairs above. For example,
   Of all the rocks on this our *planet,*
   We take too many stones for *granite.*

Part D

Choose the list or lists of words you want to learn this week.
Then complete the activities next to each list you choose.

Big Idea Words

1. Write the words given in pronunciation symbols.
   a. Aunt Hilda wants to (pri zėrv′) some strawberries.   preserve
   b. We called the restaurant to (ri zėrv′) a table.   reserve
   c. Careful planning will (en shùr′) success.   allusion
   d. An (i lü′zhən) is a misleading appearance.   illusion
   e. An (ə lü′zhən) is an indirect reference.   ensure
2. Write one pair of easily confused list words in which the
   first consonants following the vowel differ.

Challenge Words

Write the words given in pronunciation symbols.
1. A plan is (ten′tə tiv) if it is done as a trial or experiment.   preliminary
2. A boarder who stays a short time is a (tran′shənt).   tentative
3. A (tem′pə rer′ē) filling is meant to last only for a while.   temporary
4. A choice is an (ôl tėr′nə tiv).   alternative
5. A (pri lim′ə ner′ē) speech comes before the main business   transient
   of a meeting.

Content Words

Write the content word that has the same letter as the letter in
the blank in each sentence.   a. sarcasm
1. The _(d)_ of the word *portly* is stout or fat.   b. irony
2. But the _(e)_ of *portly* suggests dignity.   c. satire
3. _(c)_ is a form of writing that ridicules a habit or idea.   d. denotation
4. _(a)_ is a sneering or cutting remark.   e. connotation
5. _(b)_ occurs when the usual meaning of words is the oppo-
   site of what a speaker is thinking.

STUDY HINT!

Group your list words in pairs and study their meanings
as well as their spellings.

7

Cherish This Choice

Part A

Say the words in the list below. Write the words.

1. cherish
2. charity
3. drenched
4. mischief
5. launch
6. spinach
7. watched
8. hatch
9. scratch
10. stretch
11. batch
12. stitch
13. shudder
14. friendship
15. astonish
16. dash
17. slush
18. squash
19. chaperon *
20. mustache *

The sounds /ch/ and /sh/ can be spelled in various ways. In this lesson /ch/ is spelled **ch** and **tch,** and /sh/ is spelled **sh, ch,** and **che.**

- Write the first list word in which /ch/ is spelled **ch.**
- Write the first list word in which /ch/ is spelled **tch.**
- Write the first list word in which /sh/ is spelled **sh.**
- Write the list word in which /sh/ is spelled **ch.**
- Write the list word in which /sh/ is spelled **che.**
- Underline the letters that spell /ch/ or /sh/ in each list word.

✳Wild Words   The Greek word *mystax* meant ''upper lip.'' This word passed through Medieval Latin, Italian, and French (*moustache*) before becoming the English word *mustache*. The word *chaperon* comes from the Old French *chaperon,* meaning ''hood'' or ''protector.''

Part B

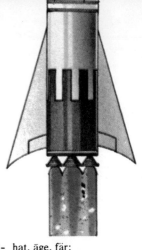

1. Write the correct list words for each category below.

    a. /ch/ spelled **ch**

    b. /ch/ spelled **tch**

    c. /sh/ spelled **sh**

    d. /sh/ spelled **ch**

2. Write the following list words shown in pronunciation symbols. In these words /ch/ or /sh/ occurs in the initial position.

    a. (chār′ə tē)
    b. (cher′ish)
    c. (shud′ər)
    d. (shap′ə rōn′)

hat, āge, fär;
let, ēqual, tėrm;
it, īce; hot, ōpen, ôrder;
oil, out; cup, pùt, rüle;
ch, child; ng, long; sh, she;
th, thin; ᴛʜ, then;
zh, measure;

ə represents *a* in about,
e in taken, *i* in pencil,
o in lemon, *u* in circus.

3. Write these list words in which /ch/ or /sh/ occurs in the medial position.

    a. (frend′ship)
    b. (mis′chif)

4. Write these list words in which /ch/ or /sh/ occurs in the final position.

    a. (lônch)
    b. (hach)
    c. (skrach)
    d. (mus′tash)
    e. (skwosh)
    f. (ə ston′ish)

WHAT'S THE BIG IDEA?

Both /ch/ and /sh/ can be spelled in various ways and can occur in the initial, medial, or final position in a word.

Dictionary

Guide words on dictionary pages can help you locate words quickly. Usually two guide words (printed in heavy boldface type) appear at the top of each dictionary page. The first guide word indicates the first word found on that page; the second guide word indicates the last word on the page. In some dictionaries one guide word is printed at the top of the outside column of every page. For example, on pages 400 and 401 of a dictionary the guide words might be *former* and *four*. All the main entries that come alphabetically between these two words can be found on those two pages.

Using your glossary, find and write the two guide words that appear on the same page as the following list words.

1. launch
2. charity
3. mischief
4. drenched
5. astonish

Rearrange the letters of the following words to form new words. Use the clues to help you, as in the example:
    name = the hair on a horse's neck: <u>mane</u>

1. door = a smell; a scent: ____
2. not = 2,000 pounds: ____
3. atom = a ditch around a castle: ____
4. oils = dirt: ____
5. broth = beat, pulsate, as in a heart: ____
6. unclear = a kind of warfare: ____
7. post = halt, cease: ____

Choose the list or lists of words you want to learn this week.
Then complete the activities next to each list you choose.

---

1. Complete these sentences, using *too* or *to.*
   Carlos went (a) the store. Mary went (b) .
2. Use *by, until,* or *from* in these sentences.
   The lost puppy was found (a) the creek.
   Horace comes (b) Mississippi.
   I can stay out (c) it's dark.

Review Words

too
to
by
until
from

---

1. Write the words in which /ch/ is spelled **ch.**
2. Write the word in which /ch/ is spelled **tch.**
3. Write the word in which /sh/ is spelled **sh.**
4. Write two list words in which /sh/ is spelled **sh.**

Big Idea Words

grouch
shrub
chimpanzee
clutch
slouch

Use a dictionary to match these challenge words with their definitions.
1. medicine that lessens nervousness or excitement ____
2. medicine used to treat diseases caused by certain bacteria ____
3. condition caused by not eating the proper foods ____
4. chronic disease of the respiratory system ____
5. device used to stop bleeding ____

Challenge Words

sedative
tourniquet
penicillin
malnutrition
asthma

⌠TUDY HIΠT!

To study your list words, group them according to the way /ch/ or /sh/ is spelled.

Where's the Trap?

Part A

Say the words in the list below. Write the words.

1. actual
2. auxiliary
3. calendar
4. favorite
5. funeral
6. interested
7. obstacle
8. privilege
9. reference
10. tentacles
11. approximately
12. definitely
13. intelligence
14. preparation
15. repetitious
16. restaurant
17. separately
18. supplemented
19. hemorrhage *
20. vandalism *

What do these list words have in common? Each word has one or more spelling traps, or problem areas. The traps are in the unaccented syllables that follow the accented syllable. The vowel sound in these unaccented syllables is /ə/, which may be spelled one way in one word and another way in another word.

- How is the vowel sound spelled in the second syllable of *restaurant?*
- How is the vowel sound spelled in the second syllable of *separately?*
- How is the vowel sound spelled in the third syllable of *approximately?*

*Wild Words   Be careful when you spell *hemorrhage* or *vandalism.* Don't forget the second **h** in *hemorrhage.* Remember to put an **a** in the second syllable of *vandalism.*

VAND LISM

Part B

The dictionary pronunciation is given for each incomplete list word shown below. In most cases vowel letters are missing from these words, but some consonants that cause spelling problems are also missing. First supply the missing letters; then write the word.

hat, āge, fär;
let, ēqual, tėrm;
it, īce; hot, ōpen, ôrder;
oil, out; cup, pùt; rüle;
ch, child; ng, long; sh, she;
th, thin; ŦH, then;
zh, measure.

ə represents *a* in about,
e in taken, *i* in pencil,
o in lemon, *u* in circus.

Words Accented on the First Syllable

1. (kal′ən dər)   cal __ __ d __ r
2. (ak′chü əl)   ac __ __ __ l
3. (def′ə nit lē)   def __ n __ tely
4. (fā′vər it)   fav __ rite
5. (fyü′nər əl)   fun __ ral
6. (in′tər ə stid)   int __ r __ sted
7. (ob′stə kəl)   obst __ cle
8. (priv′ə lij)   priv __ lege
9. (ref′ər əns)   ref __ r __ nce
10. (res′tər ənt)   rest __ __ r __ nt
11. (sep′ər it lē)   sep __ r __ tely
12. (sup′lə men tid)   supp __ __ mented
13. (ten′tə kəlz)   tent __ c __ __ s
14. (hem′ər ij)   hem __ __ __ __ age
15. (van′dl iz′əm)   vand __ __ ism

Words Accented on the Second Syllable

16. (ôg zil′yər ē)   auxil __ __ __ ry
17. (ə prok′sə mit lē) appro __ __ m __ tely
18. (in tel′ə jəns)   intel __ __ gence

Words Accented on the Third Syllable

19. (prep′ə rā′shən)   prep __ ra __ ion
20. (rep′ə tish′əs)   rep __ ti __ __ ous

WHAT'S THE BIG IDEA?

Be aware that /ə/ in an unaccented syllable may be spelled one way in one word and another way in another word.

Part B Score: _____ —20   **13**

Proofreading

A common noun is the name of any one of a group of people, places, or things *(dog, country, female)*. A proper noun is the name of a particular person, place, or thing *(Lassie, England, Ms. Roberts)*. Common nouns are not capitalized; proper nouns <u>always</u> are.

For each group of words below, decide which words should be capitalized and write them correctly.
1. city, state, illinois
2. the junior high school, carlton high school
3. governor of the state, governor kelly

Write each sentence below, writing correctly (1) the word or words that should be capitalized and (2) the misspelled word.

4. My faverite subject in school is english.
5. Vandelism at clifford high has declined recently.
6. We were intrested in the speech mayor keats gave.
7. I was definately late for my spanish class.

Supply the missing letter in this sign; then rewrite the word correctly.

14   *Part C Score:* _____ —17

Part D

Choose the list or lists of words you want to learn this week.
Then complete the activities next to each list you choose.

Rewrite these review words, supplying the missing letters.
1. de__ided
3. __s__ally
5. ___sily
2. prob____ly
4. b___utiful

Review Words

decided
probably
usually
beautiful
easily

---

1. Write the words in which the vowel sound in the second syllable is spelled **o**.
2. Write the word in which the vowel sound in the second syllable is spelled **i**.
3. Write the word in which the vowel sound in the second syllable is spelled **a**.
4. Write two list words in which the vowel sound in the second syllable is spelled **e**.

Big Idea Words

vandal
censor
patron
qualify
hypocrite

Write the content word(s) that has the same letter as the letter in the blank in each sentence.
1. The _(b)_ of an area includes hills, lakes, bridges, and roads.
2. _(a)_ is the making or study of maps or charts.
3. A _(d)_ uses colors, shading, or materials such as clay to show the different heights of a surface.
4. A _(c)_ uses lines to show heights above sea level.
5. A pilot of a ship or an airplane uses a _(e)_.

Content Words

a. cartography
b. topography
c. contour map
d. relief map
e. navigation chart

STUDY HINT!

As you study your list words, note the way in which /ə/ is spelled in each word.

15

Keep It on Ice!

Part A

Say the words in the list below. Write the words.

1. *accomplice*
2. *apprentice*
3. *entice*
4. *practice*
5. *sacrifice*
6. *service*
7. *suffice*
8. *compromise*
9. *enterprise*
10. *franchise*
11. *improvise*
12. *revise*
13. *supervise*
14. *itemize*
15. *patronize*
16. *specialize*
17. *summarize*
18. *symbolize*
19. *hypnotize* *
20. *sympathize* *

The words in this lesson end in the sounds /is/, /īs/, or /īz/. The sounds /is/ and /īs/ are spelled **ice** (as in *accomplice* and *entice*). The sounds /īz/ are spelled **ise** or **ize** (as in *compromise* and *patronize*).

- Write the list word formed by adding *-ice* to *serve.*
- Write the list word formed by adding *-ize* to *item.*
- Write the list word formed by adding *-ize* to *symbol.*
- Write the list word formed by adding *-ize* to *summary.*
- Underline the ending *-ice, -ise,* or *-ize* in each list word.

∗Wild Words   Both *hypnotize* and *sympathize* end in *-ize.* But they have more than that in common: the second letter in each word is **y.** Don't forget the **y** in *hypnotize* and *sympathize!*

Part B

hat, āge, fär;
let, ēqual, tėrm;
it, īce; hot, ōpen, ôrder;
oil, out; cup, pùt, rüle;
ch, child; ng, long; sh, she;
th, thin; ŦH, then;
zh, measure;

ə represents *a* in about,
e in taken, *i* in pencil,
o in lemon, *u* in circus.

1. For each definition below write the matching list word given in pronunciation symbols. Remember that /is/ and /īs/ are spelled **ice** while /īz/ can be spelled **ise** or **ize.**

   a. (en tīs′): tempt
   b. (sak′rə fīs): give up one thing for another
   c. (ə pren′tis): person learning a trade or art
   d. (pā′trə nīz): be a regular customer of
   e. (sə fīs′): be enough; be sufficient
   f. (en′tər prīz): project; venture; undertaking
   g. (hip′nə tīz): put into a condition resembling deep sleep
   h. (sü′pər vīz): look after and direct; manage
   i. (sim′pə thīz): feel kind feelings toward others
   j. (fran′chīz): right to vote

2. Supply the correct list word in each incomplete sentence below. Use the glossary if necessary.

   a. After arguing for an hour, we both decided to ____.
   b. Our flag and national anthem ____ our country.
   c. Mrs. Ricardo had the hospital ____ her bill.
   d. Gail had to ____ the dive again and again.
   e. Mr. Chen asked Jim to ____ his book report.

   summarize
   itemize
   symbolize
   compromise
   practice

   f. Carla plans to become a doctor; she wants to ____ in neurosurgery.
   g. We were happy with the prompt ____.
   h. Ms. Glickman asked her students to ____ their compositions and hand in the corrected versions.
   i. Without an ____, the thief could not have escaped.
   j. Pedro had to ____ a speech in drama class.

   accomplice
   service
   revise
   specialize
   improvise

WHAT'S THE BIG IDEA?

The sounds /is/ and /īs/ are spelled **ice; /īz/** can be spelled **ise** or **ize.**

Each word explained in a dictionary is an entry word. Entry words may be ordinary words, abbreviations, proper nouns, technical terms, prefixes, or suffixes. Entry words are printed in heavy boldface type and are arranged in alphabetical order (including abbreviations).

Rewrite these words, arranging them in the order in which they would appear as entry words in a dictionary.

symbolize
summarize
SW
S.A.
sacrifice

If an entry word has more than one syllable, it is written to show the syllabication, as in **en tice.** Use your glossary to rewrite these list words, dividing them as entry words would be divided.

accomplice
compromise
itemize
patronize

Use the clues to supply these words ending with *-ice.* All but two of the words are list words.

	i	c	e
		i	c	e
			i	c	e
				i	c	e
					i	c	e
						i	c	e

1. a starchy grain
2. the amount for which a thing is sold
3. tempt; lure
4. be enough
5. do something again and again
6. give up one thing for another

Part D

hat, āge, fär;
let, ēqual, tèrm;
it, īce; hot, ōpen, ôrder;
oil, out; cup, pùt, rüle;
ch, child; ng, long; sh, she;
th, thin; ŦH, then;
zh, measure;

ə represents *a* in about,
e in taken, *i* in pencil,
o in lemon, *u* in circus.

Choose the list or lists of words you want to learn this week. Then complete the activities next to each list you choose.

---

1. Supply the appropriate review words.
   a. _____ went to the show with us.
   b. Mrs. Tracy gave _____ that assignment.
2. Write the contraction for each of the following:
   a. does not
   b. do not
   c. we are

Review Words

they
doesn't
don't
we're
them

---

1. Write the word from the right that ends in *-ice*.
2. Write the word from the right that ends in *-ise*.
3. Write the word from the right formed by adding *-ize* to
   a. general   b. hospital   c. legal
4. Write the list word formed by adding *-ize* to
   a. special   b. patron

Big Idea Words

generalize
notice
hospitalize
excise
legalize

Write the content words that are shown in pronunciation symbols.
We had to (mod′ər nīz) __(1)__ the (prə sē′jər) __(2)__ in our office. The changes in (tek nol′ə jē) __(3)__ have forced us to (kəm pyü′tə rīz′) __(4)__ our financial records. This has proven to be an excellent (i kon′ə mē) __(5)__ measure.

Content Words

technology
economy
modernize
computerize
procedure

⌿TUDY HIΠT!

Group your words according to their endings (*-ice* stands for /is/ or /īs/, *-ise* stands for /īz/, and *-ize* stands for /īz/) in order to study them.

The Mass Media

Part A

Say the words in the list below. Write the words.

1. announcer
2. article
3. broadcast
4. camera
5. columnist
6. interview
7. magazine
8. network
9. newspaper
10. sponsor
11. advertisement
12. commercial
13. documentary
14. electronic
15. illustrations
16. microphone
17. propaganda
18. transmitted
19. censorship *
20. pamphlet *

The words in this lesson are associated with the mass media. The term *mass media* refers to forms of communication (such as radio, television, newspapers, and magazines) that reach large numbers, or masses, of people.

● Write five list words that may be associated with both radio and television.
● Write three list words that may be associated with both magazines and newspapers.

＊Wild Words   The sound /s/ is spelled two ways in the word *censorship:* **c** and **s.**   The word *pamphlet* came into English from the Middle English word *pamflet,* meaning "booklet." But the word goes back farther—to the Old French *Pamphilet,* which was a popular name for a Latin poem of the 1100s.

Part B

1. Complete each of the following passages using the appropriate list words.

Georgia Van Vliet is a (a) for a (b) . She is writing an (c) based on an (d) with Judy Mammon, who is a beekeeper.

newspaper
article
columnist
interview

A (e) on the life of President Roosevelt will be (f) on a major television (g) next month. The company that is the (h) of the program has decided to run one (i) at the beginning of the program and one at the end.

network
broadcast
sponsor
commercial
documentary

The television (j) looked directly at the (k) and spoke into the (l) as he read the (m) for dishwashing detergent.

microphone
announcer
advertisement
camera

The first issue of the new electronics (n) contained many diagrams and black-and-white (o) . A list of stores at which special (p) components can be purchased was also included.

electronic
illustrations
magazine

2. Supply the missing letters in the following list words; then write the words.
   a. pr__p__g__nda
   b. __en__ __rship
   c. pa__ __ __let
   d. transm__ __ __ __ed

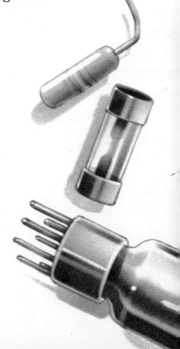

WHAT'S THE BIG IDEA?

Because the mass media affects your daily life in many ways, you should know how to spell words related to it.

Proofreading

Italics are used to set off or emphasize certain words and phrases. In longhand or typewritten manuscripts, italics are indicated by underlining. In printed material italic type (type in which the letters slant to the right) is used. Always italicize the following:

- titles of books, magazines, newspapers, pamphlets, motion pictures, and television series
- foreign words and phrases

Rewrite the sentences below, correcting the misspelled list words and underlining the titles and foreign phrases that should be italicized.

1. An artical on crime was in the New York Times.
2. Killer Bees is a dockumentery series that will be brodcast every other week.
3. The travel magazine ran an ad with illistrations of an ocean liner and a large bon voyage sign.

SPELLBOUND

The ability to spell well is valuable in a journalism or advertising career. Misspellings in print can cause confusion, misunderstanding, or even laughter. Find the misspelled word in this ad and rewrite it correctly.

FOR SALE
14 ACRES
WILL DEVELOPE FOR BUILDER
922-6200

Part D

hat, āge, fär;
let, ēqual, tèrm;
it, īce; hot, ōpen, ôrder;
oil, out; cup, put, rüle;
ch, child; ng, long; sh, she;
th, thin; ᴛʜ, then;
zh, measure;

ə represents *a* in about,
e in taken, *i* in pencil,
o in lemon, *u* in circus.

Choose the list or lists of words you want to learn this week.
Then complete the activities next to each list you choose.

Review Words

1. Write the word in which **ea** spells /ā/.
2. Write the word in which **ea** spells /ē/.
Use *their, there,* or *there's* in these sentences.
3. I parked my bike over ____.
4. ____ the book I need!
5. The Williamses are happy with ____ dune buggy.

weak
break
there
their
there's

Challenge Words

Match the challenge words with their definitions by writing
the words given in pronunciation symbols.
1. (klē shā′):   a timeworn expression or idea
2. (ə non′ə məs):   by a person whose name is not given
3. (ster′ē ə tīp):   a fixed character; conventional type
4. (süd′n im):   fictitious name used by an author
5. (yü′fə miz′əm):   use of a mild expression instead of
   one that is harsh

anonymous
pseudonym
euphemism
cliché
stereotype

Content Words

Write the content word that has the same letter as the letter in
each blank in a sentence.
1. The path over which an electric __(d)__ flows is called a
   __(a)__ .
2. __(e)__ is a form of energy that can produce light.
3. An __(b)__ is used to prevent the passage of electricity, heat,
   or sound.
4. A __(c)__ is used to change electric current to a higher or
   lower voltage.

a. circuit
b. insulator
c. transformer
d. current
e. electricity

STUDY HINT!

When you write your list words, check them over as carefully as you would if they were going to appear in print.

REVIEW

Steps to Help You Study Your Words

Before you write each word:
 Look at the word.
 Look at the letters.
 Say the word.
 Listen to the sounds.
When you write each word:
 Copy the word from your list.
 Remember how the word is spelled
  and write it.
After you write each word:
 Check the word with your list.
 Do you see any mistakes?
 Notice where the mistakes are and
  begin the steps again.

Study the review words. *(Lesson 1)*

loose	proceeding
lose	affect*
preceding	effect*

Copy them, noting trouble spots.

Choose two personal list words you
need to master. Copy them carefully.

Study the review words. *(Lesson 2)*

mischief	friendship
scratch	chaperon*
stitch	mustache*

Copy them, noting trouble spots.

Choose two personal list words you
need to master. Copy them carefully.

Study the review words. *(Lesson 3)*

obstacle	separately
privilege	hemorrhage*
restaurant	vandalism*

Copy them, noting trouble spots.

Choose two personal list words you
need to master. Copy them carefully.

Study the review words. *(Lesson 4)*

accomplice	enterprise
sacrifice	hypnotize*
compromise	sympathize*

Copy them, noting trouble spots.

Choose two personal list words you
need to master. Copy them carefully.

Study the review words. *(Lesson 5)*

broadcast	illustrations
sponsor	censorship*
advertisement	pamphlet*

Copy them, noting trouble spots.

Choose two personal list words you
need to master. Copy them carefully.

24

Work with Review Words

1. Write all the review words in alphabetical order.
2. Write the seven review words that contain double letters. Underline the double letters.
3. Write the twelve review words that have three or more consonants together. Underline the consonant combinations.

Work with Personal Words

1. Look at each personal word and identify the part that is difficult. Write each word, leaving a blank for your trouble spot. Then put your words away for one day. When you get them out, fill in the blanks.
2. Use five of your personal words in a short story or a paragraph.

Test Yourself

1. Read each sentence below. If an underlined word is misspelled for the way it is used, write it correctly.
   a. Why does he always <u>loose</u> his gloves?
   b. The bride was already <u>preceding</u> down the aisle.
   c. That book had a great <u>effect</u> on my life.
2. Find the misspelled word in each group of words and write it correctly.
   a. obstacle, sacrafice, broadcast
   b. priviledge, enterprise, friendship
   c. pamplet, mischief, vandalism
   d. proceeding, stitch, seperately
   e. chaperon, hypnitize, sacrifice
   f. simpathize, affect, scratch
   g. advertisment, accomplice, sponsor
   h. censorship, compromise, shaperon
   i. restarant, privilege, illustrations
   j. enterprise, mustashe, pamphlet
   k. separately, obstacal, sponsor
   l. stich, hemorrhage, hypnotize
   m. mustache, restaurant, sponser
   n. sympathize, sensorship, effect
   o. vandelism, preceding, lose

25

ZOUNDS GOOD

Part A

Say the words in the list below. Write the words.

1. counselor
2. society
3. ancestor
4. excellence
5. conscience
6. incident
7. necessity
8. corpuscle
9. discipline
10. fascination
11. applause
12. desert
13. deserve
14. miserable
15. enthusiasm
16. disastrous
17. exercise
18. despise
19. miscellaneous *
20. xylophone *

You probably remember that there are several spellings of /s/—for example, **s, c, sc, ss,** and **ce.** But did you know that /z/ has several spellings too, including **s, se,** and **x?** This lesson focuses on these sounds and spellings.

When we say that /s/ is spelled **ce,** we are usually referring to the /s/ spelling at the end of a word.
● Write the two list words that contain /s/ spelled **ce.**

When we say that /z/ is spelled **se,** we are usually referring to the /z/ spelling at the end of a word.
● Write the three list words that contain /z/ spelled **se.**

✻Wild Words   Remember that /s/ is spelled **sc** and **s** in *miscellaneous.*   Think of XYZ when you are spelling *xylophone.* The word begins with /z/, but its first two letters are **xy.**

*Test Score:*_____ —20   **26**   *Part A Score:*_____ —5

Part B

1. Write the following words, using **s** or **c** to spell /s/.

   a. ex__ellence   b. coun__elor   c. in__ident

2. Write the following words, using **s, se,** or **x** to spell /z/.

   a. de__ert   b. applau__   c. mi__erable
   d. __ylophone   e. enthu__ia__m   f. de__erve

3. These three list words contain both /s/ and /z/. Write them correctly.

   a. di__a__trous   b. exer__i__   c. de__pi__

4. Write the list word in which /s/ is spelled **c** and **ss.**

5. Write the two list words in which /s/ is spelled **s** and **c.**

6. Write the four list words that contain /s/ spelled **sc.**

7. Complete the following sentences with a word from your list.

   a. One of the girls in that band plays the ____.
   b. My ____ really bothered me after I lied to Dad.
   c. Swimming and ice-skating are good forms of ____.
   d. Alice has a bad cold and she feels just ____.
   e. Only a few kinds of plants can grow in a ____.
   f. Tim's ____ advised him to take French next year.
   g. Don't you think we ____ an explanation?
   h. Good nutrition is not a luxury; it's a ____.

WHAT'S THE BIG IDEA?

Both /s/ and /z/ are often spelled **s.** Other spellings of /s/ are **c, sc, ss,** and **ce;** other spellings of /z/ are **se** and **x.**

hat, āge, fär;
let, ēqual, tėrm;
it, īce; hot, ōpen, ôrder;
oil, out; cup, pút, rüle;
ch, child; ng, long; sh, she;
th, thin; ŦH, then;
zh, measure;

ə represents *a* in about,
e in taken, *i* in pencil,
o in lemon, *u* in circus.

Part C
DICTIONARY

Can you spell (zen′ə fō′bē ə), (lə vī′ə thən), (shús), or (flə meng′kō)? If not, could a dictionary help you?

It could—if you knew where to look. Many dictionaries include a chart listing the different letters that are used to spell initial sounds in words. This chart can give you a good start toward spelling unfamiliar words.

Let's try (zen′ə fō′bē ə). Turn to the spelling chart on page 136 and look next to **z.** There you see that /z/ can be spelled two ways when it is the first letter of a word: **z** or **x.** If you check the dictionary under **zen-,** you won't find the word. Check under words beginning **xen-** and you will: the word is *xenophobia*, ''fear of strangers.''

A word like (lə vī′ə thən) is a bit trickier. The chart can help with the initial letter (check and you will see that it can only be **l**). But the only way to figure out the **ə** is to look under all its possible spellings: **la, le, li,** and so on. This may take time, but eventually you will find the word: *leviathan*, ''a huge sea animal.''

Using the spelling chart and your glossary, write the correct spellings of (shús), (flə meng′kō), and (gėr′kən).

See how many list words you can place on the grid, using *counselor* as a guide.

28

Part D

Choose the list or lists of words you want to learn this week.
Then complete the activities next to each list you choose.

Fill in the blanks with the correct review word.

Review Words

1. I didn't know ____ to walk or ride.
2. Hal likes ham ____ eggs for lunch.
3. ____ dog is a mutt.
4. Amy can't go ____ she has the flu.
5. ____ would you like to go today?

Review Words
and
because
where
our
whether

---

1. Write the words in which /s/ is spelled **s.**
2. Write the word in which /s/ is spelled **sc.**
3. Write the word in which /z/ is spelled **se.**
4. Write two list words in which /s/ is spelled **s.**

Big Idea Words
correspond
semester
accuse
fluorescent
prosecute

Write the content word that has the same letter as the letter in the blank in each sentence.

Content Words
a. restrictive
b. nonrestrictive
c. subordinate
d. participle
e. gerund

1. In the sentence "Weaving is my favorite pastime," *weaving* is used as a __(e)__ .
2. In the sentence "Weaving through the traffic, he soon caught up with her," *weaving* is used as a __(d)__ .
3. A modifier is __(b)__ when it is set off by commas, as in "Robie House, built in 1909, is world famous."
4. A modifier is __(a)__ when it is not set off by commas, as in "Most houses built in 1909 had wooden floors."
5. In the sentence "Jack Reilly, who is my cousin, has red hair," *who is my cousin* is a __(c)__ clause.

Use constructions like these in five original sentences.

ʃTUDY HIΠT!

Study your list words by grouping them according to whether they contain /s/, /z/, or both /s/ and /z/.

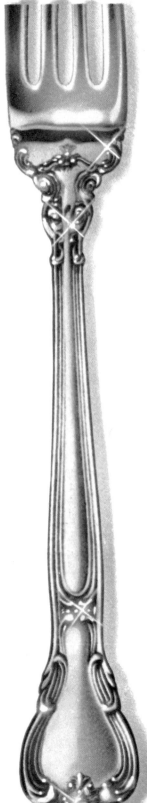

Eyeing the End

Part A

Say the words in the list below. Write the words.

1. believed
2. wasted
3. interfered
4. bandaging
5. surprising
6. patrolling
7. admitted
8. preferred
9. rebelled
10. hurried
11. satisfied
12. qualified
13. qualifying
14. marrying
15. replying
16. benefited
17. traveled
18. panicked
19. dining *
20. eyeing *

How does the spelling of a base word change when you add -ed or -ing to it? For some words, you drop the **e** and add -ed or -ing.

● Write the first two list words that follow this rule.

For other words, you double the final consonant before adding -ed or -ing, especially if the accent is on the last syllable of the base word.

● Write the first two list words that follow this rule.

For words ending in **y** preceded by a consonant, change the **y** to **i** and add -ed, but keep the **y** when adding -ing.

● Write the first two list words that follow this rule.

● Underline the two list words in which -ed is added without changing the spelling of the base word.

*Wild Words　　Drop the **e** from *dine* when adding -ed or -ing. But keep your eye on the **e** in *eye* when adding -ing.

Part B

Complete the following chart by writing in the missing spelling word. Pay close attention to what happens to the spelling of the base word when *-ed* or *-ing* is added.

BASE WORD	-ed FORM	-ing FORM
1. hurry	_____	hurrying
2. satisfy	_____	satisfying
3. marry	married	_____
4. reply	replied	_____
5. qualify	_____	_____
6. believe	_____	believing
7. waste	_____	wasting
8. interfere	_____	interfering
9. bandage	bandaged	_____
10. surprise	surprised	_____
11. dine	dined	_____
12. eye	eyed	_____

When the accent is on the final syllable of a word, you double the final consonant and add *-ed* or *-ing.*

13. admit	_____	admitting
14. prefer	_____	preferring
15. rebel	_____	rebelling
16. patrol	patrolled	_____

When the accent is on the first syllable, simply add the ending *-ed* or *-ing* to the base word.

17. benefit	_____	benefiting
18. travel	_____	traveling

If a word ends in a vowel followed by **c,** add a **k** before adding an ending starting with **e, i,** or **y.**

19. panic	_____	panicking

WHAT'S THE BIG IDEA?

Look at a word before you add *-ed* or *-ing* to it. If you're not sure whether the spelling of the base word changes, check back to the rules you've been given.

Proofreading

Two important uses of the comma are to separate nouns of direct address and to set off appositives.

Whenever you name, or "address," the person you are speaking to, separate that name from the rest of the sentence with commas. Only one comma is needed when the name comes at the beginning or at the end of a sentence. But two commas are needed when the name comes in the middle:

What are you doing, *Yvonne?*

Tonight, *my friend,* is the last time I do the dishes.

Mister, which is the way to Union Station?

An appositive is a noun, usually with modifiers, that comes right after another noun to explain it in some way. When the appositive gives additional information about the preceding noun, it is set off by commas. For example:

Trish, *my cousin,* is an architect.

Cairo, *a city in southern Illinois,* was once a stop on the Underground Railroad.

Rewrite these sentences, providing the seven missing commas and correcting the five misspelled words.

1. Al my older brother admited he was not qualifyed.
2. Cary did you like the movie?
3. The surpriseing thing Dad was that they prefered living in the coldest climate.
4. Eying our dog, our mail carrier Mr. Chang ran away.

SPELLBOUND

Read each set of words. Then write one word that, when placed in front, seems to go with each word in the set.

1. <u>head</u> + board, ache, stone
2. _____ + box, cube, cream
3. _____ + set, tan, stroke
4. _____ + brush, net, dryer
5. _____ + box, bed, pot
6. _____ + bulb, house, year
7. _____ + store, case, end
8. _____ + beam, light, shine

Part D

hat, āge, fär;
let, ēqual, tėrm;
it, īce; hot, ōpen, ôrder;
oil, out; cup, pút, rüle;
ch, child; ng, long; sh, she;
th, thin; ŦH, then;
zh, measure;

ə represents *a* in about,
e in taken, *i* in pencil,
o in lemon, *u* in circus.

Choose the list or lists of words you want to learn this week.
Then complete the activities next to each list you choose.

Big Idea Words

1. Write the two words in which the **e** is dropped before *-ed* is added.
2. Write the two words in which the **e** is dropped before *-ing* is added.
3. Write the word in which the last letter of the base word is doubled before *-ing* is added.
4. Write two list words in which the **e** is dropped before *-ing* is added.

referring
preparing
influenced
typing
evaded

Challenge Words

Use both the pronunciations and the definitions to help you write the correct challenge word.
1. (kən glom′ər it): group of unrelated businesses
2. (kôr pə rā′shən): a business group
3. (ə mal′gə māt id): combined or united
4. (mə nop′ə lē): sole control of a service or product
5. (səb sid′ē er′ē): a company having over half of its stock owned or controlled by another company

subsidiary
amalgamated
monopoly
conglomerate
corporation

Content Words

Write the content word that has the same letter as the letter in the blank in each sentence.
1. A __(d)__ is a person who worries unnecessarily that he or she is ill or is about to become ill.
2. __(a)__ is a very contagious, sometimes serious, disease.
3. Doctors __(b)__ children against measles and mumps.
4. The lungs are __(c)__ organs.
5. Hay fever is an __(e)__ reaction to pollen or ragweed.

a. influenza
b. inoculate
c. respiratory
d. hypochondriac
e. allergic

STUDY HINT!

Study your list words by concentrating on the changes in the base word when *-ed* or *-ing* is added.

What Are the Criteria?

Part A

Say the words in the list below. Write the words.

1. everyone's
2. someone's
3. world's
4. school's
5. women's
6. salesmen's
7. countries'
8. Ms. Davis's
9. the Smiths'
10. the Cashmans'
11. the Harris's
12. monkeys
13. skies
14. personalities
15. crises
16. analyses
17. criteria
18. phenomena
19. alumni *
20. stimuli *

Do irregular plurals confuse you? Do you sometimes use apostrophes to make words plural? Do you get mixed up forming singular and plural possessives? This lesson will help you with all these spelling problems.

- Apostrophes are never used to make words plural. Which of these words is not a plural? *world's   skies*
- Singular nouns form the possessive by adding **'s** to the end of the word. Which of these nouns is a singular possessive? *Ms. Davis's   countries'*
- Most irregular plurals involve a spelling change in the word; regular plurals are formed by adding *-s* or *-es*. Which of these plurals is irregular? *criteria   monkeys*
- Underline all the list words that are possessives.

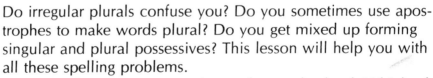

＊Wild Words   *Stimulus–stimuli* and *alumnus–alumni* kept their Latin plural forms when they came into English.

Part B

1. Write the singular possessive form of these words.
   - a. world
   - b. everyone
   - c. Ms. Davis
   - d. someone
   - e. school

2. Almost all plurals, regular or irregular, follow some pattern. Complete these patterns with list words:
   - a. *Parentheses* is to *parenthesis* as ____ is to *crisis*.
   - b. *Fungi* is to *fungus* as ____ is to *stimulus*.
   - c. *Groceries* is to *grocery* as ____ is to *personality*.
   - d. *Automata* is to *automaton* as ____ is to *criterion*.
   - e. *Turkeys* is to *turkey* as ____ is to *monkey*.

3. To form the plural possessive of a noun, first write its plural form. If the plural ends in **s,** put an apostrophe after the **s.** If the plural does not end in **s,** add **'s** to the word. Now complete this chart:

Singular	Plural	Plural Possessive
a. sky		
b. country		
c. woman		
d. salesman		
e. alumnus		
f. phenomenon		
g. analysis		

4. Plurals of names are always formed by adding *-s* or *-es* (Mr. Beman, the Beman**s**; Ms. Jones, the Jones**es**). To make a plural name possessive, simply put an apostrophe after the **s** (the Bemans**'** dog, the Joneses**'** cat).

   Using your list, make these phrases possessive.
   - a. the car of the Harrises
   - b. the house of the Smiths
   - c. the lawn of the Cashmans

WHAT'S THE BIG IDEA?

Remember the rules for forming singular and plural possessives and the patterns that plurals can follow.

Proofreading

Possessive forms of nouns are not the only words that use apostrophes; contractions use them too. In contractions the apostrophe shows that one or more letters have been left out when two words are joined. It also shows *where* letters have been left out. The apostrophe in *shouldn't,* for example, means that a letter has been omitted between the **n** and **t** (should + n[o]t = shouldn't).

Write the contractions for the following words, being careful to place the apostrophes correctly.

1. you are
2. who is
3. do not
4. it is
5. that is
6. they are

Rewrite correctly the nine words in this paragraph that have missing, misplaced, or unnecessary apostrophes.

I dont know whos' going to the dance, but I'am not. Everyones excitement about it is just plain stupid. And this schools' idea of having people dress up like monkey's for it is crazy too. They shouldn't even waste their time. I mean, its just for silly people people anyway. It doesnot even bother me that I havent got a date.

SPELLBOUND

Find the misspelled word and write it correctly.

NEW! Womens Mad-City

Part D

Choose the list or lists of words you want to learn this week. Then complete the activities next to each list you choose.

Review Words

1. Which review word is a plural?
2. Which word is a plural possessive?
3. Change each word in parentheses so that its form in the sentence is correct.
   a. The movie was (excite).
   b. I am (run) in the track meet.
   c. Don't get (excite) over nothing.

excited
exciting
friends
friends'
running

Big Idea Words

1. Write the correct plural.
   a. one trophy; two ____
   b. one genius; two ____
   c. one linguist; two ____
2. Complete the sentence with the correct possessive.
   a. The newspaper ____ assignment took him to Europe.
   b. The ____ opening statement to the jury was eloquent.
3. Write the two list words that form their plurals by changing **y** to **i** and adding *-es.*

prosecutor's
correspondent's
linguists
geniuses
trophies

Challenge Words

Use both the pronunciations and the definitions to help you write the correct challenge word.
1. (lü′də krəs): absurd; ridiculous
2. (jō′vē əl): good-humored; full of fun
3. (non′shə länt′): unconcerned; indifferent
4. (jib′ər ish): senseless chatter
5. (hwim′zə kəl): full of fanciful notions

gibberish
whimsical
jovial
nonchalant
ludicrous

STUDY HINT!

Study your list words by putting them into three groups: singular possessives, plural possessives, and plurals.

To What Degree?

Part A

Say the words in the list below. Write the words.

1. *earlier*
2. *friendlier*
3. *funniest*
4. *healthier*
5. *hungrier*
6. *loneliest*
7. *sneakier*
8. *ugliest*
9. *choicest*
10. *truer*

11. *fastest*
12. *sooner*
13. *straightest*
14. *stricter*
15. *weirdest*
16. *further*
17. *farther*
18. *farthest*
19. *more brilliant* ✱
20. *less harmful* ✱

To form the comparative degree of adjectives and adverbs, either add an *-er* ending *(sooner),* or use the word *more* or *less (more brilliant).* Do not use both; for example, do not say *more stricter.* To form the superlative, either add an *-est* ending *(weirdest),* or use the word *most* or *least (least harmful).* Do not use both; for example, do not say *least straightest.*
● Underline each *-er* and *-est* ending in your list words.
● Write the list word that means "the most swift."
● The word *far* has two forms in the superlative degree—*farthest* and *furthest.* Write its comparative forms.

✱**Wild Words**   For some words—like *brilliant* and *harmful*—you cannot form the comparative and superlative degrees by adding *-er* and *-est.* They need *more* or *less* for the comparative, and *most* or *least* for the superlative.

Part B

1. To form the comparative and superlative forms of modifiers ending in **y,** change the **y** to **i** and add *-er* for the comparative, and *-est* for the superlative. Complete the following chart with the correct list word.

POSITIVE FORM	COMPARATIVE FORM	SUPERLATIVE FORM
a. early	_____	earliest
b. friendly	_____	friendliest
c. funny	funnier	_____
d. healthy	_____	healthiest
e. hungry	_____	hungriest
f. lonely	lonelier	_____
g. sneaky	_____	sneakiest
h. ugly	uglier	_____

2. When making comparisons between two persons, things, or groups, use the comparative degree. Use the superlative degree for three or more. Read the following sentences and write the correct comparative or superlative form of the word in parentheses.

   a. Which can run *(fast)*—camels, rabbits, or tigers?
   b. Maggie arrived *(soon)* than Tom.
   c. Which is the *(straight)* route—Route A, B, or C?
   d. The *(choice)* of the three rooms faces the ocean.
   e. Jones is a *(strict)* coach than Davis is.
   f. Is a rattlesnake *(harmful)* than a python?
   g. His second statement was *(true)* to the facts.
   h. Some stars seem *(brilliant)* than others.
   i. Which blazer looks *(weird)*—the tweed, the denim, or the corduroy?

3. Write the comparative and superlative forms from your list for the word *far.*

WHAT'S THE BIG IDEA?

Remember that the comparative degree is for comparing two things, and the superlative degree for three or more.

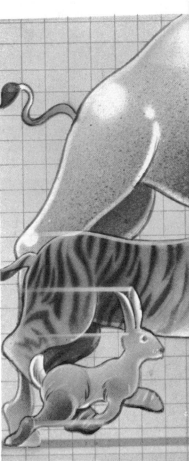

Part C
Proofreading

The letters **l** and **e**, when poorly written, can result in spelling and reading problems. Be sure that when writing **l**'s and **e**'s you make the **l** larger than the **e**.

Rewrite the following sentences, correcting the seven misspellings and forming **l**'s and **e**'s clearly.

1. The longer I wait to eat the hungarier I get.
2. My cousin Brad is sneakeier than my two brothers.
3. That company makes the uglest dolls.
4. That tie is the funnyest thing I've ever seen.
5. Irma was freindlier before she became president.
6. The earlyer we arrive, the better seats we'll have.
7. I feel healther now that I practice yoga.

Palindromes are words that spell the same word forwards or backwards—like *mom, peep,* and *Otto.* See if you can think of palindromes, using these clues.

1. the night before
2. sound of breaking balloon
3. a female sheep
4. short for father
5. Mrs., ma'am
6. sound from a horn
7. looks at; views
8. napkin for a baby's neck
9. small child
10. thing done; brave act

Part D

Choose the list or lists of words you want to learn this week.
Then complete the activities next to each list you choose.

1. Write the ordinal numbers for each of these cardinal numbers: (a) one; (b) four; (c) eight 2. If you ate as much as you wanted, you would have had ___ to eat. 3. *Thought* is the past tense of ___.	**Review Words** think fourth eighth enough first
1. Write the words that show the comparative degree. 2. Write the words that show the superlative degree. 3. Write the two list words that show the comparative degree by adding a word rather than an ending.	**Big Idea Words** more active most practical heavier more accurately heaviest
Fill in the blanks in the following sentences with the correct challenge word. 1. You can buy lunch meats, pickles, cheeses, and smoked fish at a ___. 2. Lotus blossoms, clouds' ears, and bean curds might be considered ___ foods. 3. Shish kebab is chunks of meat broiled on a ___. 4. A ___ of art appreciates fine paintings. 5. A tall glass filled with ice cream, crushed fruit, and whipped cream is called a ___.	**Challenge Words** parfait exotic skewer connoisseur delicatessen

⌐STUDY HINT!

Arrange your list words into groups according to whether they are in the comparative or superlative degree.

You, the Consumer

Part A

Say the words in the list below. Write the words.

1. amount
2. bargain
3. cashier
4. clerk
5. consumer
6. discount
7. expensive
8. financial
9. label
10. luxury
11. market
12. merchandise
13. purchase
14. quality
15. refund
16. retail
17. warehouse
18. wholesale
19. guarantee *
20. warranty *

All of your list words have to do with the buying and selling of products. Some of the words—like *cashier, clerk,* and *consumer*—designate people who buy and sell. Other words—like *bargain* and *discount*—refer to prices one might pay. And other words—like *market* and *warehouse*—refer to places where items can be bought.

● Write the list word that means "goods for sale."
● Write the list word that means "to buy something."

*Wild Words   Which would you rather have—a 30-day *guarantee* or a 30-day *warranty?* A *guarantee* is a pledge by a manufacturer to replace or repair a product if you don't believe the product lives up to claims made for it. A *warranty* is a pledge by a manufacturer to repair or replace defective parts in a product within defined limits—for example, within thirty days or five thousand miles.

Test Score:_____ —20   **42**   Part A Score:_____ —2

Part B

1. Write the three list words with the letter sequence **ou.**

2. Write the two list words with the letter sequence **ai.**

3. Write the two list words with the letter sequence **ua.**

4. Write the list word with the letter sequence **ia.**

5. Write the list word with the letter sequence **ie.**

6. Write the list word with the letter sequence **uxu.**

7. Above each group of sentences are five words. Read each sentence; write the word that best completes it.

expensive   merchandise   bargain   label   refund
   a. A cheap but poorly made item is not really a ____.
   b. Large stores can offer ____ in many price ranges.
   c. "We will ____ your money if you are not satisfied."
   d. One result of inflation is that goods and services become more ____.
   e. A ____ on an item often tells what it is made of.

quality   amount   clerk   consumer   guarantee
   f. A ____ is a person who sells goods in a store.
   g. A ____ is a person who buys and uses those goods.
   h. The ____ a dollar can buy is decreasing rapidly.
   i. A high price is not always a proof of high ____.
   j. Buying an item with a ____ is usually a good idea.

wholesale   financial   market   warranty   purchase
   k. A ____ is a place where goods are bought and sold.
   l. Certain parts of a car are usually under ____.
   m. Always shop around before making a big ____.
   n. The ____ price is $8; the retail price is $12.
   o. A ____ expert can help people with money problems.

WHAT'S THE BIG IDEA?

Learning words having to do with buying and selling can help you become a more informed consumer.

hat, āge, fär;
let, ēqual, tėrm;
it, īce; hot, ōpen, ôrder;
oil, out; cup, pùt, rüle;
ch, child; ng, long; sh, she;
th, thin; ŦH, then;
zh, measure;

ə represents *a* in about,
e in taken, *i* in pencil,
o in lemon, *u* in circus.

Dictionary

Accent marks are used in dictionaries to show which syllables are stressed when a word is pronounced. In any word of two or more syllables the syllable that receives the strongest stress is given a primary accent. This is shown either by a heavy accent mark (ek spen′siv) or, in a few dictionaries, by a small line before and above the stressed syllable (ek ′spen siv). If another syllable in the word receives medium stress, it is given a secondary accent. The secondary accent will be marked either with a lighter accent mark (wer′hous′) or with a small line before and below the stressed syllable (′wer ˌhous).

Pronounce each of the following list words; then choose the word that best completes each statement below them and write it.

(bär′gən)   (kən sü′mər)   (gar′ən tē′)   (ka shir′)

1. _____ has two syllables with the primary accent on the last syllable.
2. _____ has two syllables with the primary accent on the first syllable.
3. _____ has three syllables with the primary accent on the last syllable and a secondary accent on the first syllable.
4. _____ has three syllables with the primary accent on the second syllable.

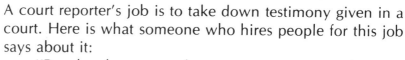

A court reporter's job is to take down testimony given in a court. Here is what someone who hires people for this job says about it:

"People who want to be court reporters must have a background, from school or work, in the legal area. But they must also have first-rate language skills, especially in spelling and mechanics. A court reporter who misspells words or forgets punctuation could seriously affect the outcome of a trial. We want applicants who have both a legal background *and* the best language skills."

Part D

hat, āge, fär;
let, ēqual, tėrm;
it, īce; hot, ōpen, ôrder;
oil, out; cup, pút, rüle;
ch, child; ng, long; sh, she;
th, thin; ŦH, then;
zh, measure;

ə represents *a* in about,
e in taken, *i* in pencil,
o in lemon, *u* in circus.

Choose the list or lists of words you want to learn this week.
Then complete the activities next to each list you choose.

Review Words

business
equipment
money
principle
trouble

1. Write the two-syllable words.
2. Write the three-syllable words.

Write the challenge words that appear in pronunciation symbols in the sentences below.

Challenge Words

economical
extravagant
exorbitant
frugal
meager

1. If you are a bargain hunter who spends money carefully, you are both (ek′ə nom′ə kəl) _(a)_ and (frü′gəl) _(b)_ .
2. If you love luxury and spend money freely, you are (ek strav′ə gənt).
3. If you have little money to spend because you get a low salary, your salary is said to be (mē′gər).
4. The word (ek strav′ə gənt) _(a)_ is an antonym for the word (frü′gəl) _(b)_ .
5. A synonym for *high-priced* is (eg zôr′bə tənt).

Write the content word that has the same letter as the letter in the blank in each sentence.

Content Words

a. nutritive
b. consumerism
c. microwave
d. cutlery
e. culinary

1. An electromagnetic wave is a _(c)_ .
2. _(d)_ consists of knives, forks, and spoons.
3. _(e)_ skill has to do with cooking or the kitchen.
4. If a food has _(a)_ value, it is nourishing.
5. _(b)_ is a trend toward increased protection of the consumer's rights.

STUDY HINT!

Learn these list words and their meanings; then use this knowledge when you purchase products.

Steps to Help You Study Your Words

Before you write each word:
    Look at the word.
    Look at the letters.
    Say the word.
    Listen to the sounds.
When you write each word:
    Copy the word from your list.
    Remember how the word is spelled
      and write it.
After you write each word:
    Check the word with your list.
    Do you see any mistakes?
    Notice where the mistakes are and
      begin the steps again.

Study the review words. *(Lesson 7)*

counselor	exercise
conscience	miscellaneous*
discipline	xylophone*

Copy them, noting trouble spots.

Choose two personal list words you need to master. Copy them carefully.

Study the review words. *(Lesson 8)*

interfered	benefited
surprising	dining*
patrolling	eyeing*

Copy them, noting trouble spots.

Choose two personal list words you need to master. Copy them carefully.

Study the review words. *(Lesson 9)*

someone's	monkeys
school's	alumni*
countries'	stimuli*

Copy them, noting trouble spots.

Choose two personal list words you need to master. Copy them carefully.

Study the review words. *(Lesson 10)*

earlier	farther
fastest	more brilliant*
stricter	less harmful*

Copy them, noting trouble spots.

Choose two personal list words you need to master. Copy them carefully.

Study the review words. *(Lesson 11)*

amount	luxury
expensive	guarantee*
label	warranty*

Copy them, noting trouble spots.

Choose two personal list words you need to master. Copy them carefully.

Work with Review Words

1. Pronounce the review words. In one list write the twelve words that have one or two syllables, and in another list write the eighteen review words with three, four, or five syllables.
2. List the thirteen review words that have the sound /s/ in them.

Work with Personal Words

1. Write a short play or skit using your personal words.
2. Alphabetize your ten personal words.
3. Select some of your personal words and arrange them on a grid, one below the other, so that the name of a city or country appears as you read down. For example:

```
R E P A I R
  B A N A N A
S T R I K E
C A N I N E
R I S K Y
```

Test Yourself

1. Read each sentence below. Find the misspelled review word and rewrite it correctly.
   a. The light was more brillianter on the beach.
   b. Someones car is blocking our driveway.
   c. An undisclosed amaunt of money was missing.
   d. Mr. Ozu, our camp counciler, was from Portland.
   e. Some groups demanded strictor discipline.
   f. Several countrie's teams won gold medals.
   g. New tax laws benefitted every taxpayer.
   h. We'll have to drive a little farthur.

2. Find the correct spelling for each word and write it.
   a. interferred, interfeared, interfered
   b. earlier, earlyer, earler
   c. lucksury, lugsury, luxury
   d. alumnie, alumni, alumny
   e. patrolling, patroleing, patroling
   f. dinning, dining, dineing
   g. warranty, warrenty, warrantie
   h. xylophone, zylophone, xylofone
   i. monkies, monkeyes, monkeys
   j. label, lable, labul
   k. garantee, garanty, guarantee

THE SHY Y

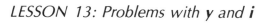

Part A

Say the words in the list below. Write the words.

1. *applying*
2. *babyish*
3. *betrayed*
4. *betrays*
5. *dyeing*
6. *laying*
7. *prying*
8. *shyest*
9. *allied*
10. *applied*
11. *dried*
12. *likelihood*
13. *marriage*
14. *pried*
15. *studies*
16. *dying*
17. *lying*
18. *tying*
19. *skiing* *
20. *taxiing* *

What happens to the **y** at the end of a word when an ending is added to the word? In many words ending in **y** no spelling change occurs before an ending is added.

● Write the list word formed by adding *-ing* to *apply*.

In some words ending in **y** the **y** is changed to **i** before an ending is added.

● Write the list word formed by adding *-ed* to *ally*.

In one-syllable words ending in **ie** the **ie** is changed to **y** before an ending is added.

● Write the list word formed by adding *-ing* to *die*.

● Underline all the *-ing* endings in your list words.

***Wild Words**   Remember the two **i**'s in the words *skiing* and *taxiing*. Skiing is a sport—it has nothing to do with the sky. Taxiing is done by a plane on a runway—it has nothing to do with government taxing.

Part B

1. For base words ending in /ē/ or /ī/ spelled **y** in which **y** follows a consonant, change **y** to **i** before adding an ending—unless the ending starts with **i.**

    Write the list words formed by combining
    a. marry + age b. ally + ed c. study + es
    d. likely + hood e. dry + ed f. apply + ed
    g. apply + ing h. pry + ed i. pry + ing
    j. baby + ish
    k. An exception to this rule is the word *shy*. Write the list word formed by adding *-est* to *shy*.

2. For base words ending in two vowels, just add the ending to the base word. Write these list words:
    a. dye + ing b. betray + ed
    c. betray + s d. lay + ing

    However, for one-syllable words ending in **ie,** change **ie** to **y** before adding *-ing*. Write these list words:
    e. lie + ing f. die + ing g. tie + ing

3. Some base words ending in /ē/ spelled **i** keep the **i** when *-ing* is added. The **i** is retained because it represents the vowel sound in the syllable in which it occurs. Write the indicated list words.
    a. ski + ing b. taxi + ing

WHAT'S THE BIG IDEA?

Avoid confusion by following these guidelines when adding endings to base words ending in /ē/ or /ī/ spelled **y,** ending in two vowels, or ending in /ē/ spelled **i.**

DICTIONARY

Many English words have variant spellings (two or more accepted ways of spelling the same word). When the variant spellings fall together alphabetically and have the same pronunciation and inflected forms, they are combined into one dictionary entry with the more common spelling given first:

di a logue or **di a log** (dī′ə lôg, dī′ə log), *n.* **1** conversation . . . .

When the spellings come together alphabetically but the pronunciations or inflected forms are different, the variants are given separate entries. The definition is given with the more common spelling:

i o din (ī′ə dən), *n.* iodine.
i o dine (ī′ə dīn, ī′ə dən, ī′ə dēn′), *n.* **1** a nonmetallic element . . . .

When variants do not occur together alphabetically, they must be entered in different parts of the dictionary. The definition is given with the more common spelling, and the less common spelling is shown in boldface type at the end of the entry:

rac coon (ra kün′), *n.* **1** a small, grayish flesh-eating mammal with a bushy, ringed tail . . . . Also, **racoon.**
ra coon (ra kün′), *n.* raccoon.

Using your glossary, find and write the more common spelling for each pair of variant spellings below.

1. taxiing—taxying
2. counselor—counsellor
3. cantaloup—cantaloupe
4. moustache—mustache
5. chaperon—chaperone
6. theatre—theater

This game is called hinky-pinky because the rhyming pairs have two syllables each (for example, a bunny custom = rabbit habit). Can you figure out these hinky-pinkies?
1. a ridiculous goat = ____
2. spoiled cloth = ____
3. margarine knife = ____

Part D

Choose the list or lists of words you want to learn this week.
Then complete the activities next to each list you choose.

1. Write the two-syllable word. 2. Write the three-syllable words. 3. Write the four-syllable word. 4. Write a sentence for each word.	**Review Words** already religion repetition practically receipt

1. Write the letter(s) representing the sound /ē/; then write the word.   **Big Idea Words**
   - a. visibilit___
   - b. captivit___
   - c. specialt___s
   - d. harmon___
   - e. jock___
2. Which list word follows the same pattern as *specialties?*

Big Idea Words
specialties
jockey
harmony
captivity
visibility

Write the challenge word that has the same letter as the letter in the blank in each sentence.   **Challenge Words**

1. __(b)__ is a sky-blue or greenish-blue mineral of gem value.
2. __(d)__ is a bright blue precious stone.
3. Transparent __(e)__ is used as a gem.
4. __(a)__ is a purple or violet variety of quartz.
5. __(c)__ is a semiprecious variety of quartz having bands of different colors.

Challenge Words
a. amethyst
b. turquoise
c. onyx
d. sapphire
e. zircon

STUDY HINT!

Group your words according to the ways endings have been added: **y** changed to **i**, **ie** changed to **y**, no change.

O, U Ought to Know

Mountainous

Part A

Say the words in the list below. Write the words.

1. outrageous
2. outwit
3. clout
4. mountainous
5. grouchy
6. slouched
7. scoundrel
8. accountant
9. dumfounded
10. pronoun
11. surroundings
12. undoubtedly
13. browse
14. coward
15. vowel
16. drowned
17. prowling
18. cauliflower
19. sought *
20. trough *

In most of your list words the sound /ou/ is spelled **ou** or **ow**.

- Write the first two list words in which the sound /ou/ is spelled **ou**.
- Write the first list word in which the sound /ou/ is spelled **ow**.

Sometimes, as in the suffix *-ous*, **ou** is pronounced /ə/.

- Write the list word with the suffix *-ous* that means "covered with mountain ranges."
- Write the list word with the suffix *-ous* that means "very offensive or insulting."

- Underline each spelling of the sound /ou/ that occurs in your list words.

*Wild Words   The sound /ô/ in *sought* is spelled **ough**.
The sound /ô/ in *trough* is spelled **ou**.

Part B

1. For each sentence below write the list word given in pronunciation symbols. Use the glossary if you need additional help.

   a. An (ə koun′tənt) prepared their income tax forms.
   b. I get (grou′chē) if I don't get enough sleep.
   c. Bonnie can (out wit′) the computer at chess.
   d. Which is a (prō′noun)—*its* or *it's?*
   e. The weary troops (sloucht) back to camp.
   f. The lodge was built in pleasant (sə roun′dingz).
   g. You, (un dou′tid lē), believe in flying saucers.
   h. The boxer had (kô′lə flou′ ər) ears.
   i. My dog becomes a (kou′ərd) if he sees a rabbit.
   j. The jet's noise (dround) out what she said.
   k. Two cats were (proul′ing) around in the alley.
   l. Which word has the (vou′əl) sound /ou/?
   m. The news of the award left me (dum′found′id).
   n. I like to (brouz) around in antique shops.
   o. "Give that ball a (klout)!" the coach shouted.
   p. The (skoun′drəl) tied his victim to the tracks.

2. Write the two list words in which the letters **ou** are pronounced /ô/ as in *cough.*

3. Write the two list words that each have two **ou**'s—one pronounced /ou/ and one pronounced /ə/.

4. In which list word is **gh** pronounced /f/?

5. In which list word is /ô/ spelled **ough?**

WHAT'S THE BIG IDEA?

Though most of the time the letters **ou** are pronounced /ou/, they are sometimes pronounced in other ways.

Dictionary
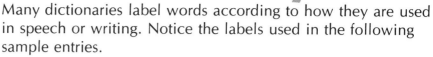

Many dictionaries label words according to how they are used in speech or writing. Notice the labels used in the following sample entries.

nos y (nō′zē), . . . INFORMAL. **1** prying or inquisitive. . . .
cool (kül), . . . **7** SLANG. admirable; excellent.
grig (grig), . . . DIALECT. **1** cricket. **2** grasshopper.

The label INFORMAL means that the word is usually used only in everyday speech and writing, but not in formal speech or writing. The label SLANG means that the word and its particular meaning are used only in very informal speech and writing. The label DIALECT indicates that the word or a certain meaning of it is used only in the speech of a particular geographical area.

Look up these words in your glossary. Then write the label you find in each entry.

1. goner
2. crackpot
3. kid
4. poke
5. clout
6. grouchy

grig (grig),... DIALECT.

Find the misspelled word in this picture and rewrite it correctly.

Part D

Choose the list or lists of words you want to learn this week. Then complete the activities next to each list you choose.

Supply the missing letters; then write the words.

Review Words

1. sh_____d
2. j____l____s
3. c____rage____s
4. c_____tr____s
5. th__r_____

thorough
countries
courageous
should
jealous

---

1. Write the letters that spell the sound /ou/ in these words given in pronunciation symbols. Write the word.
   a. (prou′is)
   b. (froun′ing)
   c. (koun′tə nəns)
   d. (drout)
   e. (prō′noun)
2. Write two list words in which /ou/ is spelled **ow.**

Big Idea Words

drought
countenance
pronoun
prowess
frowning

Write the challenge word that has the same letter as the letter in the blank in each sentence.

Challenge Words

1. A writ of _(a)_ requires that a prisoner be brought before a judge to determine if he or she is being held lawfully.
2. An order from a higher court to a lower one is a _(b)_ .
3. Someone who receives a _(d)_ must appear before a court to give testimony.
4. A rule or law made by authority is an _(e)_ .
5. A summons to appear before a court of law is a _(c)_ .

a. habeas corpus
b. mandate
c. citation
d. subpoena
e. ordinance

ʃTUDY HINT!

Study your list words by grouping them according to how the sound /ou/ in them is spelled: **ou** or **ow.**

Notice the Difference

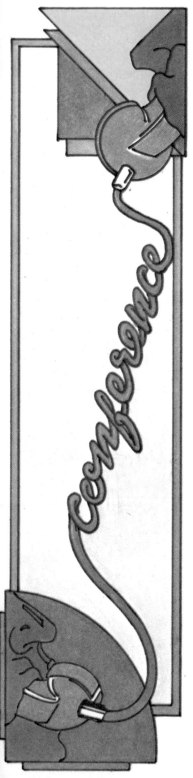

Part A

Say the words in the list below. Write the words.

1. acquaintance
2. allowance
3. importance
4. inheritance
5. reliance
6. conference
7. correspondence
8. difference
9. preference
10. assistant
11. ignorant
12. observant
13. dependent
14. persistent
15. accuracy
16. bankruptcy
17. inadequacy
18. literacy
19. hypocrisy *
20. controversy *

Adding a suffix to a base word will change the base word's meaning. When you add *-ant* to the verb *assist* ("to give help") the new word, *assistant,* means "one who gives help." When you add *-ence* to the verb *confer* ("to discuss or talk over") the new word, *conference,* means "a meeting for discussing or talking over." Notice that letters may be changed or dropped from a base word when suffixes are added.

● Write the list word that means "having the quality of being accurate."
● Write the list word that means "the act of inheriting."
● Underline the *-ant* suffixes in your list words.

✳Wild Words *Hypocrisy* and *controversy* are the only list words that do not have suffixes. *Hypocrisy* means "a pretending to be what one is not"; a *controversy* is "an argument involving opposing views." Both words end in **sy.**

Part B

1. When *-ance* or *-ence* is added to a verb, the word formed is a noun. Write the nouns formed from these verbs. Notice any spelling changes that occur in the verb forms when the suffix is added.
   - a. acquaint   +   *-ance*   =
   - b. import   +   *-ance*   =
   - c. rely   +   *-ance*   =
   - d. allow   +   *-ance*   =
   - e. inherit   +   *-ance*   =
   - f. prefer   +   *-ence*   =
   - g. correspond   +   *-ence*   =
   - h. confer   +   *-ence*   =
   - i. differ   +   *-ence*   =

2. When *-ant* or *-ent* is added to a verb, the word formed is a noun or an adjective. Write the nouns or adjectives formed from these verbs. Notice any spelling changes that occur in the verb forms when the suffix is added.
   - a. observe   +   *-ant*   =
   - b. assist   +   *-ant*   =
   - c. ignore   +   *-ant*   =
   - d. persist   +   *-ent*   =
   - e. depend   +   *-ent*   =

3. When *-cy* is added to a noun or an adjective, the word formed is a noun. Write the nouns formed from these adjectives. Notice any spelling changes that occur in the adjective forms when the suffix is added.
   - a. literate   +   *-cy*   =
   - b. accurate   +   *-cy*   =
   - c. bankrupt   +   *-cy*   =
   - d. inadequate   +   *-cy*   =

4. Write the two list words that end in **sy**.

WHAT'S THE BIG IDEA?

Spelling changes often occur when the suffixes
-ance, -ence, -ant, -ent, and *-cy* are added to words.

Proofreading

Be sure to write clearly the letter **v** and the letter **x** in words. Read the following sentences, and find the six misspelled list words. Then write the entire sentence, spelling each word correctly and remembering to form **v**'s and **x**'s properly.

1. The help of your asistant at the confrence was a great convenience for me.
2. I couldn't tell the diffrence in quality between the cheap and the expensive xylophones.
3. The surveillance of my aquaintance caused great controvercy.
4. I cannot stress enough the importence of daily exercise.

SPELLBOUND

Use the clues to supply these words ending with *-ance*. Four words are from your list; one is not.

		a	n	c	e		
			a	n	c	e	
				a	n	c	e
				a	n	c	e
					a	n	c	e

1. love affair
2. trust or dependence
3. money for one's weekly expenses
4. significance
5. money from one's ancestors

Part D

Choose the list or lists of words you want to learn this week.
Then complete the activities next to each list you choose.

Big Idea Words

1. Add *-ence* to *confide.* What happens to the second **e?**
2. Add *-ant* to *propel.* What letter is doubled?
3. Change the *-ant* in *elegant* to *-ance.*
4. Change the *-ence* in *evidence* to *-ent.*
5. Change the final **t** in *transparent* to *-cy.*
6. Write two list words that end in *-cy.*

elegance
confidence
propellant
transparency
evident

Challenge Words

Write the challenge words given in pronunciation symbols.
1. The bubbles in soda pop give it (ef′ər ves′ns).
2. Light without much heat is (lü′mə nes′nt).
3. Something that quickly changes is (mər kyùr′ē əl).
4. Snow crystals (sin′tl āt) in the sun like diamonds.
5. To go beyond normal limits or expectations is to
   (tran send′) something.

scintillate
mercurial
effervescence
transcend
luminescent

Content Words

Using the letter clues after each sentence, supply the content
word that names the literary technique that is italicized in
each sentence.
1. The sunflower *lifted its face* to the sun.   (b)
2. I'm so tired *I could sleep for a year.*   (a)
3. *P*eter *P*iper *p*icked a *p*eck of *p*ickled *p*eppers.   (c)
4. The be*e*s buzz*e*d nois*i*ly.   (e)
5. He's *as strong as an ox.*   (d)

a. hyperbole
b. personification
c. alliteration
d. analogy
e. assonance

STUDY HINT!

Study your list words by grouping them according to their
endings: *-ance, -ence, -ant, -ent, -cy,* and *-sy.*

It's Fair Fare

Part A

Say the words in the list below. Write the words.

1. boarder
2. border
3. cell
4. sell
5. coarse
6. course
7. fair
8. fare
9. forth
10. fourth
11. grate
12. great
13. manner
14. manor
15. poles
16. polls
17. rain
18. reign
19. wind *
20. wound *

The pairs of words in this lesson are homophones—that is, they are words that are pronounced in the same way but have different spellings and meanings. Writing one homophone when you mean the other can be a spelling problem.

● Which list word means "main house of a large estate"?
● Which list word means "place where votes are cast"?
● Underline the letter or sequence of letters that is different in each pair of list words.

*Wild Words   The word (wind) means "air in motion" and (wīnd) means "twist or turn around something," but both are spelled *wind.* The word (wünd) means "an injury" and (wound) is a past tense of (wīnd), but both are spelled *wound.* The words (wind) and (wīnd), (wünd) and (wound) are homographs—words with the same spelling but different origins and meanings.

Test Score:_____ —20   **60**   Part A Score:_____ —20

Part B

1. Complete these sentences with the correct homophone from the list.

   a. The bus ____ was recently raised to 55¢.
   b. Mary was the only person still on the golf ____.
   c. On election day the ____ open at six o'clock.
   d. We cleaned the ____ in the fireplace.
   e. My brother came in ____ in the race.
   f. Queen Victoria's ____ lasted from 1837 to 1901.
   g. Tulips were planted along the ____ of the lawn.
   h. The prison ____ was cold and damp.
   i. Some kinds of sandpaper are extremely ____.
   j. One of his ski ____ was buried in the snow.
   k. Her ____ was kind and gentle—except when she was angry.
   l. Our whole family enjoys going to the state ____.
   m. The new ____ always pays his rent on time.
   n. The summer ____ lasted only a few minutes.
   o. A long tree-lined walk led up to the ____.
   p. After 85,000 miles Sue finally decided to ____ her car.
   q. Pat and Gene never argued from that day ____.
   r. Don't you feel ____ when spring finally arrives?

2. Choose the pronunciation you would use in saying each sentence below and write its letter. Then write the word that the pronunciation stands for.

   W. (wind)   X. (wīnd)   Y. (wound)   Z. (wünd)
   a. The ____ in her leg hurt.
   b. The strong ____ blew the tree over.
   c. He ____ the watch too much and it broke.
   d. ____ the rope around that pole.

WHAT'S THE BIG IDEA?

Be careful in your writing that you do not use one homophone when you mean the other.

hat, āge, fär;
let, ēqual, tėrm;
it, īce; hot, ōpen, ôrder;
oil, out; cup, pùt, rüle;
ch, child; ng, long; sh, she;
th, thin; ŦH, then;
zh, measure;

ə represents *a* in about,
e in taken, *i* in pencil,
o in lemon, *u* in circus.

Part C
Dictionary

Most dictionaries have a complete pronunciation key at the front of the book and a partial key on every second page of the book. The key's purpose is to help you make sense of the various symbols and letter combinations that the dictionary uses in its pronunciations. For example, the pronunciation the dictionary gives for *auspicious,* a word meaning "favorable; of good omen," is (ô spish′əs). If you weren't sure how to say /ô/, you could check the key for a word in which /ô/ is used. You would find *ôrder,* which would tell you that the **au** in *auspicious* is pronounced like the **o** in *order.*

Practice using the pronunciation key by writing the words that the following pronunciations represent.

1. (az)	2. (ās)	3. (kärt′n)
4. (kär tün′)	5. (klôth)	6. (klōŦH)
7. (ded)	8. (dēd)	9. (füd)
10. (fėr′nish)	11. (hīd)	12. (un′yən)
13. (pik′chər)	14. (pich′ər)	15. (plezh′ər)

SPELLBOUND

English has many homophones, and if you think about it you will realize that you know a good number of them. Test yourself by listing the homophones for the following words.

1. be	2. bred	3. I
4. knew	5. mail	6. one
7. or	8. pour	9. reed
10. sea	11. ware	12. would

Part D

Choose the list or lists of words you want to learn this week.
Then complete the activities next to each list you choose.

Remember the rule "**i** before **e** except after **c** or when the
sound is /ā/ as in *neighbor* or *weigh*"?
1. Write the three review words that follow the rule.
2. Write the two review words that do not follow the rule.

Review Words

received
seize
conscience
deceive
prairie

---

1. Which (sē′ling) is opposite the floor?
2. Which (sē′ling) means "closing tightly"?
3. Which (wāv) is a ridge of water?
4. Which (wāv) means "to give up a claim"?
5. This (strāt) is a narrow channel of water.
6. Can you spell the other (strāt)?
7. Write the two list words that are pronounced (rān).

Big Idea Words

wave
waive
sealing
ceiling
strait

Write the content word that best completes each sentence.
1. All of the new citizens recited the pledge of ____.
2. Seven nations finally signed the peace ____.
3. When it became clear that no agreement could be reached,
   the ____ were broken off.
4. Símon Bolívar defeated the Spanish in Venezuela and is
   remembered as the ____ of that country.
5. A good judge does not take sides; in other words, he or she
   is ____.

Content Words

treaty
liberator
allegiance
impartial
negotiations

STUDY HINT!

Study your list words as pairs of homophones and know how
each is used.

63

A Day in Court

Part A

Say the words in the list below. Write the words.

1. accused
2. acquittal
3. alibi
4. attorney
5. court
6. defendant
7. evidence
8. guilty
9. innocent
10. jury

11. oath
12. perjury
13. plea
14. prosecution
15. testify
16. testimony
17. verdict
18. witness
19. indictment *
20. misdemeanor *

All the words in this lesson are terms used in law. Some of the words describe people involved in a trial—*attorney, defendant, witness.* Other words describe elements of a trial—*evidence, plea, testimony.* And others describe judgments made in a trial—*acquittal, guilty,* or *innocent.*
● Write the list word that means "an excuse."
● Write the list word that means "a group of people selected to hear evidence and make a judgment in court."
● Write the list word that means "lying under oath."

✳Wild Words   Remember that **ct** spells the sound /t/ in *indictment*—a formal, written accusation.   A *misdemeanor* is a minor crime, such as a traffic violation.

Part B

hat, āge, fär;
let, ēqual, tėrm;
it, īce; hot, ōpen, ôrder;
oil, out; cup, pút, rüle;
ch, child; ng, long; sh, she;
th, thin; ŦH, then;
zh, measure;

ə represents *a* in about,
e in taken, *i* in pencil,
o in lemon, *u* in circus.

1. Use the pronunciation symbols in parentheses to write the correct list words.

   a. Will you (tes′tə fī) that you saw the car go through the red light?
   b. His (al′ə bī) was confirmed by the waiter.
   c. The (kôrt) adjourned until Monday morning.
   d. The (pros′ə kyü′shən) presented (ev′ə dəns) that was quite circumstantial.
   e. The (di fen′dənt) was found not (gil′tē) on three charges of disturbing the peace.
   f. Before giving her (tes′tə mō′nē), Smith was reminded that she was still under (ōth).
   g. They both entered a (plē) of (in′ə sənt) to the charge of embezzling.
   h. Exceeding the speed limit is a (mis′di mē′nər).
   i. The grand (jür′ē) brought an (in dīt′mənt) against two of the suspects.

2. If you have to divide a word in which two consonant letters appear together, a syllable break occurs between the consonants (as in *sen-tence*). Look at these pairs of list words; then copy those words that are divided correctly between the two consonant letters. You may check your glossary.

   a. a-ccused
   b. ac-cused
   c. ac-quit-tal
   d. acq-ui-ttal
   e. att-orney
   f. at-tor-ney
   g. per-jur-y
   h. perj-ur-y
   i. verd-ict
   j. ver-dict
   k. wit-ness
   l. wi-t-ness

3. Write the two list words that spell the sound /s/ with the letter **c** or the letters **ce**.

WHAT'S THE BIG IDEA?

Because law can affect your life in important ways, you should know how to spell some of the words related to it.

Part B Score:_____ —22   **65**

Proofreading

To make a plural noun show possession, do this: First write the plural form. If it ends in **s,** put an apostrophe after the **s.** If the plural does not end in **s,** add **'s** to the end of the word. Now complete this chart.

Singular	Plural	Plural Possessive
1. defendant	____	____
2. attorney	____	____
3. woman	____	____
4. court	____	____
5. sheep	____	____
6. witness	____	____

Proofread the following paragraph. Rewrite the six misspelled list words, and correct the three incorrect plural possessives.

The inditement accused them of kidnaping. Though during the trial the prosacution proved that the mens's alabis were false, the defendants's plee was still that they were innocent. Their attorneys's pleas for mercy were ignored, however, and the joury found the men guilty.

One job a law clerk does is to research previous cases for a lawyer and write up briefs, or summaries, of them. Here is what one lawyer in a firm that hires law clerks says about the job:

"Of course, anyone who works in law must be able to spell well, and not just the lawyers, but also the law clerks who write up briefs. I might have to read dozens of briefs and I just don't have the time to stumble over bad spelling when I read them over. . . . There's also a risk involved if someone I hire can't spell. If he or she misspells a name or an important word or two in a case—well, that kind of mistake can jeopardize my defense of a client."

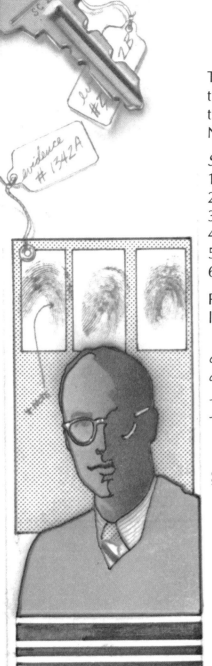

Part D

Choose the list or lists of words you want to learn this week. Then complete the activities next to each list you choose.

1. Divide into syllables the two words with double **m**'s.
2. Divide into syllables the word with a double **e**.
3. Write the review word that has only one syllable.
4. Write the word that means "look over and change."

Review Words

right
revise
summary
commit
career

Write the challenge words given in pronunciation symbols in these sentences.

1. The words *forsooth* and *methinks* are (är kā′ik).
2. The term (mē′dē ē′vəl) refers to the period of history from about A.D. 500 to A.D. 1450.
3. The great revival of art and learning between about A.D. 1300 and A.D. 1600 is called the (ren′ə säns′).
4. A regent is someone who governs in place of an absent ruler, and that government is called a (rē′jən sē).
5. The (gil′ə tēn′) was named after Joseph I. Guillotin.

Challenge Words

Renaissance
medieval
guillotine
archaic
regency

Write the content word that has the same letter as the letters in the blanks in each sentence.

1. The _(d)_ refers to the eleven southern states that seceded from the Union in 1860–1861.
2. The _(c)_ _(e)_, issued on January 1, 1863, by Abraham Lincoln, declared the _(b)_ of _(a)_ in any state then in armed rebellion against the United States.

Content Words

a. slavery
b. abolition
c. Emancipation
d. Secession
e. Proclamation

STUDY HINT!

Study your list words and learn their meanings so you'll know more about law.

R E V I E W

Steps to Help You Study Your Words

Before you write each word:
  Look at the word.
  Look at the letters.
  Say the word.
  Listen to the sounds.
When you write each word:
  Copy the word from your list.
  Remember how the word is spelled
    and write it.
After you write each word:
  Check the word with your list.
  Do you see any mistakes?
  Notice where the mistakes are and
    begin the steps again.

Study the review words. *(Lesson 13)*

dyeing	dying
likelihood	skiing✱
marriage	taxiing✱

Copy them, noting trouble spots.

_____

Choose two personal list words you
need to master. Copy them carefully.

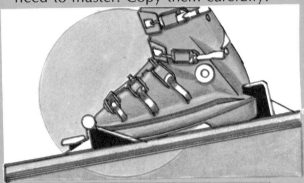

Study the review words. *(Lesson 14)*

outrageous	cauliflower
dumfounded	sought✱
drowned	trough✱

Copy them, noting trouble spots.

_____

Choose two personal list words you
need to master. Copy them carefully.

Study the review words. *(Lesson 15)*

reliance	inadequacy
correspondence	hypocrisy✱
ignorant	controversy✱

Copy them, noting trouble spots.

_____

Choose two personal list words you
need to master. Copy them carefully.

Study the review words. *(Lesson 16)*

boarder	fourth
border	wind✱
forth	wound✱

Copy them, noting trouble spots.

_____

Choose two personal list words you
need to master. Copy them carefully.

Study the review words. *(Lesson 17)*

acquittal	prosecution
guilty	indictment✱
innocent	misdemeanor✱

Copy them, noting trouble spots.

_____

Choose two personal list words you
need to master. Copy them carefully.

Work with Review Words

1. Write all the review words in alphabetical order.
2. Write the six review words that contain the vowel combination **ou.** Underline the **ou** in each word.
3. Write the nine review words that have either (1) a double **i** or (2) **i** and another vowel together (for example, v**ei**l, d**ia**ry). Underline each vowel combination.

Work with Personal Words

1. Print your ten personal words, leaving a blank space for each vowel. Then go back and fill in the blanks.
2. Make a word search puzzle in which at least six of your ten personal words appear. Remember that words may appear across, down, or diagonally—forwards or backwards. Use the puzzle at the right as a guide.

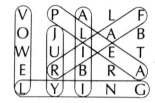

Test Yourself

1. Find the correct spelling of each word and write it.
   a. inditement, indictement, indictment
   b. controversy, contravercy, controvercy
   c. corespondence, correspondense, correspondence
   d. misdemeenor, misdemeanor, misdemeaner
   e. liklyhood, likelyhood, likelihood
   f. inadaquacy, inadaquasy, inadequacy
2. Decide which underlined word, if any, is misspelled (or spelled incorrectly for the way it is used) in the following sentences. Write the number of the misspelled word; then write the word correctly. If no word is misspelled, write the number 4.
   a. He was [1]dumfounded that I was so [2]ignarant about basic [3]skiing techniques. [4]None
   b. Although our [1]boarder [2]sought, to appear humble, his [3]hypocrasy was known to everyone. [4]None
   c. The [1]fourth year she had a garden, she put in a [2]border of [3]cauliflower plants. [4]None
   d. Even the lawyer for the [1]prosecution was not sure if they were [2]innosent or [3]guilty. [4]None
   e. [1]Outrageous as it seems, there is a great [2]likelihood that the children [3]drownded. [4]None

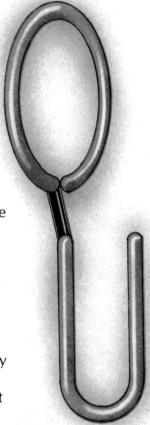

SUPERMARKET

COMPOUND INTEREST

Part A

4 word sentences

original

Say the words in the list below. Write the words.

1. by-product
2. part-time
3. no-hitter
4. close-up
5. no one
6. home plate
7. grade school
8. doorknob
9. homeroom
10. myself

11. nobody
12. sawdust
13. somewhere
14. supermarket
15. whatever
16. workout
17. teenager
18. fiberglass
19. all right *
20. teammate *

A new word formed by combining two or more words is called a *compound word*.

Some compounds are written with hyphens between the words. These are called *hyphenated compounds*.
● Write the first hyphenated compound on the list.

Some compounds are written as separate words but are thought of as one word. These are called *open compounds*.
● Write the first open compound on the list.

And many compounds are written as one word. These are called *closed compounds*.
● Write the first closed compound on the list.

*Wild Words   *All right* can be used as an adjective or as an adverb, but it should always be written as two separate words.   Remember that just as players on a team work together, keep the words *team* and *mate* together.

Test Score: _____ —20   **70**   Part A Score: _____ —3

Part B

1. Combine a word from Column A with one from Column B to form a compound from your spelling list. Be sure you join the words in each compound correctly. Notice there are two groups of words in each column.

Column A	Column B	Compound Words
a. by	plate	
b. close	hitter	
c. home	time	
d. door	product	
e. part	up	
f. no	knob	
g. no	dust	
h. team	school	
i. saw	one	
j. what	where	
k. grade	ager	
l. some	mate	
m. teen	ever	

2. Most closed compounds can be divided at the end of a line after the first word in the compound. Rewrite these list words, using a hyphen to indicate how the words should be divided at the end of a line.

   a. homeroom   b. myself   c. nobody
   d. fiberglass   e. supermarket   f. workout

3. If the open compound *all right* is written as *alright,* it's not only incorrectly changed to a closed compound but also misspelled. Write the correct form.

WHAT'S THE BIG IDEA?

Even though compound words are considered single words, they can be written three different ways: together, with hyphens, or separated.

BIG LEAGUE BUBBLE GUM

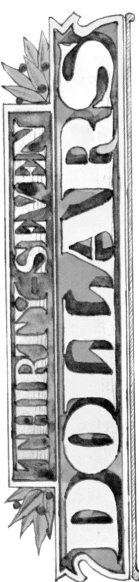

Part C

PROOFREADING

In addition to punctuating certain compound words, we commonly use hyphens in these ways:

- with written numbers from twenty-one to ninety-nine:
  thirty-seven dollars   two hundred *sixty-four* days
- with fractions used as modifiers:
  three-fifths majority   *one-third* full
  Note: Fractions used as nouns can be written with or without hyphens:
  Only two thirds (*or* two-thirds) of the seats were sold.
  I was in the top one fourth (*or* one-fourth) of my class.
- with a compound modifier *preceding* a noun:
  first-base umpire   an *I-told-you-so* look
  dark-blue suit   *meat-eating* birds
  Note: If a compound modifier comes *after* the noun, or if its first part ends in *-ly,* no hyphen is used:
  The umpire on *first base* wore a suit of *dark blue.*
  The *beautifully dressed* singer took her bow.

Proofread the following sentences. Then rewrite each sentence, spelling correctly the two incorrectly written list words and inserting the five missing hyphens.

1. My next door neighbor says canned goods at the super-market are marked one third off.

2. As for my self, I take a grin and bear it attitude.

Find the incorrectly written
list word in this picture and
rewrite it correctly.

Choose the list or lists of words you want to learn this week.
Then complete the activities next to each list you choose.

---

1. Write a review word that means the opposite of each of the
   following words or phrases.
   a. no one   b. sooner
   c. after   d. a few
2. Which review word means "through the whole time of"?

Review Words
someone
during
a lot
later
before

---

1. Write the open compound word.
2. Write the two closed compound words.
3. Write the two hyphenated compound words.
4. Write two open compounds from the spelling list.

Big Idea Words
waterproof
thunderstorm
cross-reference
water moccasin
free-lance

Write the challenge word that has the same letter as the letter
in the blank in each sentence.
1. Machinery will _(e)_ if it is not maintained well.
2. With a fresh coat of paint, new shingles, and trimmed
   shrubbery, the house no longer looked _(d)_ .
3. Poor eating habits and little exercise, among other things,
   will prove a _(c)_ to one's health.
4. The act of intentionally injuring another person so he is
   less able to defend himself is the crime of _(a)_ .
5. Immediately following the earthquake, _(b)_ broke out in
   the central area of the city.

Challenge Words
a. mayhem
b. pandemonium
c. detriment
d. dilapidated
e. deteriorate

⌠TUDY HINT!

Study your list words by grouping them according to the
kinds of compounds they are: open, closed, or hyphenated.

Watch Your Language

Part A

Say the words in the list below. Write the words.

1. language
2. suffrage
3. usage
4. wreckage
5. deliberate
6. dominate
7. evaporate
8. ultimate
9. anniversary
10. dictionary
11. literary
12. cemetery
13. machinery
14. shrubbery
15. slavery
16. dormitory
17. history
18. victory
19. itinerary *
20. mileage *

A suffix may be added to a recognizable English base word to form a new word, as *wreck* + *-age* become *wreckage,* and *slave* + *-ery* become *slavery.* But sometimes a word with a suffix has no recognizable base in English—such as *language.* That's because the ending was already part of the word in the language from which it's derived.

- Write the list word that comes from the Latin word *suffragium* meaning "supporting vote."
- Write the list word that comes from the Latin word *anniversarius* meaning "returning annually."
- Underline the endings *-age, -ate, -ary, -ery,* and *-ory* in the list words.

*Wild Words Breaking *i-tin-e-rar-y* into syllables should help you to spell it correctly. Remember to keep the *-age* at the end of *mile.*

Test Score: _____ —20   **74**   Part A Score: _____ —22

Part B

Read the sentences after each group of list words. Then complete the sentences with the correct word.

language   suffrage   usage   wreckage   mileage

1. Linguistics is the scientific study of ____.
2. That car looks like it's had some pretty rough ____.
3. For one thing the ____ is over ninety thousand miles.
4. And it looks like it was put together from ____.
5. The Nineteenth Amendment granted ____ to women.

deliberate   dominate   evaporate   ultimate

6. Water will ____ at 212 degrees Fahrenheit.
7. Three skyscrapers ____ the view of Chicago's skyline.
8. "What you said was a ____ lie!" he shouted.
9. The ____ result was that we ended up in first place.

anniversary   dictionary   literary   itinerary

10. This ____ translates Italian words into English.
11. My ____ includes stops in Boston and Cambridge.
12. Next week they celebrate their tenth wedding ____.
13. Her first novel was judged a ____ masterpiece.

cemetery   machinery   shrubbery   slavery

14. Ancient Romans often sold prisoners into ____.
15. Johnny spent the morning trimming the ____.
16. ____ comes from the Latin word for "sleeping place."
17. That new ____ produces ten thousand yoyos an hour.

dormitory   history   victory

18. That last ____ clinched the pennant for the Reds.
19. In Toronto we slept in the college ____.
20. This statue's ____ goes back to 1583.

WHAT'S THE BIG IDEA?

Sometimes words with suffixes do not have recognizable English bases. You have to memorize their spelling.

Part C
Proofreading

When writing words that have a **g** or a **q** in them, be sure to form each letter carefully. A poorly formed **g** can very easily be mistaken for a **q.** Practice these two letters by writing these words.

language   *request*   *qualify*
wreckage   *inquire*   *usage*

Read the following sentences. Then rewrite each sentence, correctly spelling the four misspelled list words. Remember to form **g**'s and **q**'s clearly.

1. *I get quite good milage with my car.*
2. *Your dictunary will answer any questions you have on the meanings of these litary terms.*
3. *The queen quivered and quaked when she learned that the expected victory turned into defeat.*

SPELLBOUND

The words in capital letters in the sentences below are a portion of a list word. From that clue and the context of the sentence, write the correct list word for each.
1. TIM ATE the last chocolate doughnut.
2. I used RUBBER gloves when I trimmed the hedges.
3. The VAPOR condensed on the cold windowpanes.
4. ANN celebrated her birthday yesterday.
5. He got hit on the CHIN by the rotating camshaft.
6. During my trip, I took a tour of a TIN mine.

Choose the list or lists of words you want to learn this week.
Then complete the activities next to each list you choose.

---

1. In which word is *-ing* added with no change to the base word?
2. In which word is the final consonant doubled before *-ing* is added?
3. In which word is the final **e** dropped before *-ing* is added?
4. What is the past tense of (a) pay; (b) lead?

Review Words
beginning
dining
hurrying
paid
led

---

1. Fill in the blanks with the correct words from the right.
   a. Is ____ part of Olympic competition?
   b. Tea is a favored ____ of the British.
   c. She scored well on the ____ skating events.
   d. Because they use less fuel, ____ size cars are becoming very popular.
   e. Learning ten new words a week will increase your ____.
2. Write three list words that end in *-ery*.

Big Idea Words
intermediate
compulsory
beverage
vocabulary
archery

Write the content word that has the same letter as the letter in the blank in each sentence.
1. During the power failure, the hospital relied on its own _(d)_ for electricity.
2. The divers used a _(e)_ to fill their tanks with air.
3. She cut a _(a)_ for the corner of the frame.
4. A device for receiving and storing an electrical charge is a _(b)_.
5. The parts of the bicycle were indicated on the _(c)_.

Content Words
a. miter joint
b. capacitor
c. diagram
d. generator
e. compressor

STUDY HINT!

Study your list words by grouping them according to their endings: *-age*, *-ate*, *-ary*, *-ery*, and *-ory*.

Doubles, Anyone?

Part A

Say the words in the list below. Write the words.

1. addressed
2. aggravate
3. aggressive
4. appreciation
5. attitude
6. challenge
7. commotion
8. difficult
9. exaggerate
10. misspell
11. necessary
12. occasionally
13. occurrence
14. opportunity
15. professional
16. shuttle
17. squirrels
18. stubbornness
19. parallel *
20. sheriff *

Forgetting where the double consonants appear in these words can cause spelling problems, but this clue may help you avoid confusion: double consonants often follow short vowel sounds.

- Write the list word that has a double **g** and a double **s** and means "very active; energetic."
- Write the list word that has a double **c** and a double **l** and means "now and then."
- Underline the double consonants in the list words. Note that some words may contain more than one set.

✳Wild Words Sometimes you may know that a word contains double letters, but you may not be sure <u>which</u> letters to double. Remember where the double **l** appears in *parallel*—don't double the **l** at the end of the word. The word *sheriff* has a double **f,** not a double **r.**

Part B

The dictionary pronunciation is given for each incomplete list word shown below. First supply the missing consonant letters; then write the word.

1. (ag′rə vāt)   a＿＿ravate
2. (shut′l)   shu＿＿le
3. (kə mō′shən)   co＿＿otion
4. (ə gres′iv)   a＿＿re＿＿ive
5. (op′ər tü′nə tē)   o＿＿ortunity
6. (stub′ərn nes)   stu＿＿or＿＿e＿＿
7. (ə kėr′əns)   o＿＿u＿＿ence
8. (par′ə lel)   para＿＿el
9. (nes′ə ser′ē)   nece＿＿ary
10. (dif′ə kult)   di＿＿icult
11. (chal′ənj)   cha＿＿enge
12. (ə drest′)   a＿＿re＿＿ed
13. (at′ə tüd)   a＿＿itude
14. (prə fesh′ə nəl)   profe＿＿ional
15. (skwėr′əlz)   squi＿＿els
16. (sher′if)   sheri＿＿
17. (eg zaj′ə rāt′)   exa＿＿erate
18. (ə prē′shē ā′shən) a＿＿reciation
19. (mis spel′)   mi＿＿pe＿＿
20. (ə kā′zhə nəl ē)   o＿＿asiona＿＿y

WHAT'S THE BIG IDEA?

In each of your list words two consonant letters spell a single consonant sound. Don't let this cause confusion when you spell the words.

Dictionary

You already know that when a word has to be divided at the end of a line of writing it should be divided at a syllable break. When a word contains double consonants, a syllable break usually occurs between them (as in the words *at-torney* and *in-nocent*). However, if the double consonants come at the end of a base word, the consonants are usually not split (as in *fall-ing* or *buzz-er*).

Rewrite these list words, using a hyphen to indicate how the words should be divided at the end of a line.

1. shuttle   2. aggressive
3. misspelled   4. stubbornness
5. squirrels   6. occurrence
7. challenge   8. addressed

SPELLBOUND

Fill in the missing letters in the following puzzles. The clues will help you figure out the incomplete words.

_TT____ = fall upon with force

___TT____ = rabbit food

_____TT__ = a weaver's device

___TT__ = a written message

___TT_ = sentence adopted as a rule of conduct

___LL___ = a color

___LL___ = a column

___LL___ = a bank clerk

___LL___ = telephoned

___LL___ = having nothing inside; empty

Make your own puzzle using other double consonants.

Part D

hat, āge, fär;
let, ēqual, tėrm;
it, īce; hot, ōpen, ôrder;
oil, out; cup, pùt, rüle;
ch, child; ng, long; sh, she;
th, thin; ᴛʜ, then;
zh, measure;

ə represents *a* in about,
e in taken, *i* in pencil,
o in lemon, *u* in circus.

Choose the list or lists of words you want to learn this week.
Then complete the activities next to each list you choose.

Supply the missing letters; then write the word.

Review Words

1. po_____ible
2. o_____osite
3. proc_____d
4. inte_____upt
5. po_____e_____ion

possession
proceed
possible
opposite
interrupt

---

1. Write the words given in pronunciation symbols.
   a. I used a scarf as an (ak ses′ər ē).
   b. Rain and cold weather (di pres′) me.
   c. Thinking requires the use of (in′tə lek′chü əl) powers.
   d. We studied (nar′ə tiv) poetry.
   e. Max and Joan (pə zes′) a talent for singing.
2. Write the list word that has a double **c** and double **l,** and
   the list word that has a double **b** and double **s.**

Big Idea Words

possess
accessory
depress
intellectual
narrative

Read the definitions below. Then write the content word that
has the same letter as the letter in the blank in each definition.

Content Words

1. country in North Africa (d)
2. an island continent (c)
3. country in southwest Asia (b)
4. islands in the Pacific (a)
5. country in South America (e)

a. Philippines
b. Afghanistan
c. Australia
d. Libya
e. Uruguay

STUDY HINT!

To study your words, organize them according to their
double consonants: **dd, ss, gg, pp, tt, ll, mm, ff, cc,
rr, bb,** and **nn.**

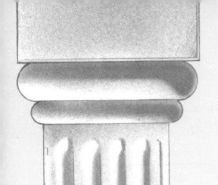

It's Greek to Me

Part A

Say the words in the list below. Write the words.

1. *automatic*
2. *autograph*
3. *autobiography*
4. *biography*
5. *biology*
6. *chronic*
7. *chronometer*
8. *democracy*
9. *geography*
10. *geology*
11. *geometry*
12. *phonograph*
13. *telephone*
14. *telegraph*
15. *thermometer*
16. *thermostat*
17. *static*
18. *theology*
19. *atheist* ✱
20. *epidemic* ✱

All your list words have at least one word part that comes from Greek. Knowing just a few of these Greek word forms can help you learn the meanings of many unfamiliar words.

● If the Greek form *chron* means "time," which of these words means "lasts a long time"? *chronic static*
● If the Greek form *auto* means "self," which of these words means "works by itself"? *chronic automatic*
● If the Greek form *stat* means "stand; stabilize," which word means "not changing; at rest"? *automatic static*

✱**Wild Words** *Atheist* and *epidemic* each contain a Greek prefix as well as a Greek word form. *Atheist* is derived from the prefix *a-* ("not") + *the* ("god") and means "person who does not believe in God." *Epidemic* comes from the prefix *epi-* ("among") + *dem* ("people") and means "rapid spread of a disease among a large group of people."

Test Score: _____ —20   **82**   Part A Score: _____ —3

Part B

auto: self
bio: life
geo: earth
logy: study of
cracy: rule

chron, chrono: time
dem, demo: people
phon, phono: sound
tele: far, distant
the, theo: god

thermo: heat, temperature
graph, graphy: writing, describing, recording
meter, metry: measure
stat: stand, stabilize

Find in the chart above the Greek form for each underlined word in these sentences. Then complete each sentence with the list word that contains that Greek form or forms.

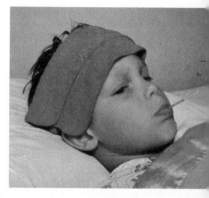

1. If a timer is ____, it shuts off by it<u>self</u>.
2. ____ electricity is stationary; it "<u>stands</u>" in air.
3. A ____ illness is an illness that lasts a long <u>time</u>.
4. In a ____, the <u>people rule</u>.
5. A ____ is a clock that <u>measures time</u> very precisely.
6. All he plays on his ____ is <u>recorded</u> jungle <u>sounds</u>.
7. __(a)__ is the <u>study of God</u>; __(b)__ is the <u>study of life</u>.
8. A book <u>written</u> about a person's <u>life</u> is a ____.
9. A book <u>written</u> about a person's <u>life</u> by the person him<u>self</u> is an ____.
10. A ____ is a device that <u>measures temperature</u>.
11. A ____ is a device that <u>keeps the temperature stable</u>.
12. The Greeks used ____ to <u>measure</u> the size of the <u>earth</u>.
13. If Chris Evert gives you her ____, she her<u>self writes</u> her name on something for you.
14. A ____ book contains <u>descriptions</u> of the peoples, countries, and resources of the <u>earth</u>.
15. ____ is the <u>study of the earth</u>'s crust.
16. A flu ____ can spread quickly among many <u>people</u>.
17. An ____ does not believe in <u>God</u>.
18. A __(a)__ can transmit the <u>sound</u> of voices over long <u>distances</u>; a __(b)__ can transmit a <u>written</u> message over long <u>distances</u>.

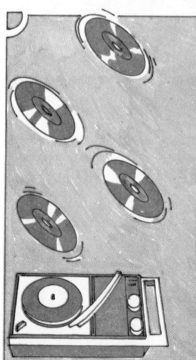

WHAT'S THE BIG IDEA?

Learning a few basic Greek word forms can help you figure out the meanings of many unfamiliar English words.

Proofreading

The period is a basic punctuation mark. It is used:
- to mark the ends of sentences: Sue fell. Answer me.
- after initials and abbreviations:
   Prof. Van A. Lewis, Jr.   B.C.   Corp.   Sept.
- between dollars and cents when a dollar sign is used:
   $.45 $208.36

Write each of the twelve items in the paragraph below that need periods, and put a period after each of them. Then write the six misspelled words correctly.

Once I got sick during a flu epademic My doctor, Dr P D Foy, kept me in bed for a week Every day at 8 AM Mom put a themometer in my mouth Then I watched quiz shows and found I was an expert on giografy I talked on the telephon a lot, and played Mom's old fonograf Best of all, Dad bought me a $1095 (ten dollars and ninety-five cents) biography of Willie Mays That made being sick almost fun!

Now that you know a few basic Greek word parts, see how many of these questions you can answer. (Check the chart in Part B if you need to.)

1. If *mega* means "large," what does a <u>megaphone</u> do?
2. If *crypto* means "secret," what is a <u>cryptograph</u>?
3. Why do some skiers wear <u>thermal</u> underwear?
4. If *micro* means "little," what is <u>microbiology</u>?
5. What kind of pictures would a <u>telephoto</u> lens be used to take? How do you know?
6. If *poly* means "many," what is a <u>polytheist</u>?

Part D

Choose the list or lists of words you want to learn this week.
Then complete the activities next to each list you choose.

Here are more words that come from Greek.

Big Idea Words

1. pseud ("false") + onym ("name") = ____
2. philo ("love of") + sophy ("wisdom") = ____
3. syn ("together") + thesis ("put; place") = ____
4. Which word means "a play"? ____
5. Which word means "science of plant life"? ____

synthesis
drama
botany
philosophy
pseudonym

Challenge Words

1. Franz A. Mesmer popularized hypnotism. Which challenge word means "hypnotize"?
2. Kharisma is Greek for "favor; divine gift." Which challenge word means "great personal appeal or charm"?
3. The gods punished the Greek king Tantalus by surrounding him with branches of fruit that sprang away whenever he tried to eat. Which challenge word means "torment"?
4. Ego is the Latin word for "I." Which challenge word means "too concerned with oneself; conceited"?
5. The Greek district called Magnesia contained minerals that could attract and hold iron. Which challenge word means "ability to attract or influence"?

tantalize
magnetism
charisma
mesmerize
egotistic

Content Words

Write the content word that has the same letter as the letter in the blank in each sentence.

1. A picture made of several distinct pictures is a _(a)_ .
2. A _(d)_ is a place where art objects are exhibited.
3. A _(e)_ is a portable case for papers and drawings.
4. _(b)_ is a method of printing designs on cloth.
5. A small enclosed three-dimensional scene is a _(c)_ .

a. montage
b. batik
c. diorama
d. gallery
e. portfolio

STUDY HINT!

Study your list words by saying each word, spelling it out loud, and then writing it. Hear and see each syllable.

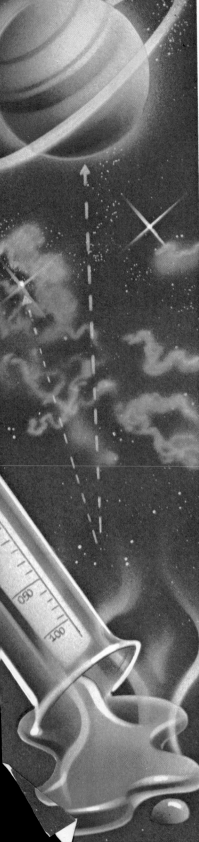

What's Your Theory?

Part A

Say the words in the list below. Write the words.

1. alcohol
2. apparatus
3. astronomy
4. botanist
5. chemist
6. eclipse
7. experiment
8. hygiene
9. laboratory
10. microscope
11. molecule
12. nebula
13. nucleus
14. radioactive
15. research
16. species
17. theory
18. vacuum
19. neutrons *
20. photosynthesis *

Did you know that there have been more discoveries made in science in the past fifty years than in all other years of recorded history? All your list words relate to science. Some refer to the study of stars—*astronomy, eclipse, nebula.* Some refer to biology and chemistry—*molecule, species, nucleus.* Some describe the work done in science—*experiment, research, theory.* And some refer to other areas of science.

● Write the list word that means "the study of stars."
● Write the list word that means "make trials or test out something."
● Write the list word that means "a careful or systematic hunting for facts or truth."

*Wild Words   Remember that **eu** spells /ü/ in *neutrons.* Breaking *pho-to-syn-the-sis* into syllables should help you to spell it correctly.

Part B

Read the sentences after each group of list words. Then complete the sentences with the correct word.

nebula   vacuum   eclipse   astronomy
1. Scientists study the sun's corona during an _____.
2. A cloudlike cluster of stars is called a _____.
3. Since fire needs air, it will not burn in a _____.
4. Astrology and _____ both deal with studying stars.

species   photosynthesis   botanist   research
5. The _____ worked at the botanical gardens.
6. Wheat is a _____ of grass.
7. A by-product of a plant's _____ is oxygen.
8. A zoologist does _____ on animal life.

nucleus   neutrons   microscope   radioactive
9. Radium is a _____ metallic element.
10. An atom is made up of protons, electrons, and _____.
11. The _____ is the center of an atom.
12. A virus can only be seen with an electron _____.

experiment   chemist   alcohol   molecule
13. A pharmacist is called a _____ in England.
14. A rubdown with _____ can help reduce a high fever.
15. Scientists can test out a theory with an _____.
16. A _____ of an element consists of one or more like atoms.

apparatus   hygiene   laboratory   theory
17. Isaac Newton proposed the _____ of gravitation.
18. _____ is the science of maintaining good health.
19. You'll find test tubes and beakers in a _____.
20. An automobile is a complicated _____.

WHAT'S THE BIG IDEA?

Since science affects your life in important ways, you should learn to spell some of the words related to it.

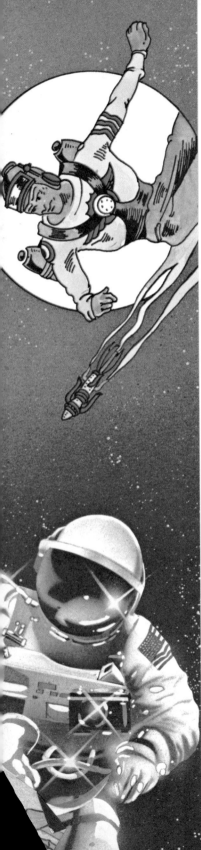

Dictionary

Dictionaries do not always give definitions for all the words that begin with a prefix. If the words can be understood by combining the meaning of the prefix with the meaning of the base word, then those words may be listed without a definition.

If you look up the definition of a word with a prefix—*unopposed,* for example—and do not find it as a separate entry, look up the base word *oppose* ("be against") and add the meaning of the prefix *un-.* Here are the meanings of two common prefixes.

re-, *prefix.* **1** again; anew; once more: *Reappear = appear again.* **2** back: *Repay = pay back.* Also, sometimes before vowels, **red-.**

un-, *prefix.* not ____; the opposite of ____: *Unequal = not equal; the opposite of equal. Unchanged = not changed. Unjust = not just.*

Look up the meaning of each base word below in the glossary. Then add to it the meaning of the prefix preceding it. Finally, write the new word and its meaning.

1. un- + discernible = ____
2. un- + liquefied = ____
3. un- + ceasing = ____
4. re- + emerge = ____
5. re- + issued = ____
6. re- + wind = ____

SPELLBOUND

Three common Greek forms that appear in some of your list words are *astro-* ("star"), *micro-* ("small"), and *photo-* ("light"). Use the following forms and clues to write new words.

1. astro- + a person who travels in space
2. micro- + film for taking small photographs
3. photo- + a meter for measuring light intensity

Part D

Choose the list or lists of words you want to learn this week.
Then complete the activities next to each list you choose.

What letters are missing? Write the whole word.
1. ar___ment
2. d_s___se
3. env_r___ment
4. s___e___le
5. p___sic___

Review Words
disease
physical
environment
argument
schedule

Write the correct challenge words in this paragraph.

 If you combine the study of word origins, etymology, with the study of animal life, (1) , you'll find some interesting items. (2) , for instance, comes from the Greek words *rhinos* ("nose") + *keras* ("horn"). *Hys,* the Greek word for "hog," in English is (3) , a wolflike mammal. The Spanish word *armado* ("armed one") is the source of (4) , an animal with its own armor. And finally, the Hindustani word *chītā* in English is the animal spelled (5) .

Challenge Words
rhinoceros
armadillo
cheetah
hyena
zoology

Write the content word that has the same letter as the letter in the blank in each sentence.
1. Some compounds of (e) are used in making matches.
2. (d) is one of the most abundant elements in the earth's crust.
3. The **H** in the formula H_2O stands for (c) .
4. Because it burns brightly, (b) is often used in fireworks.
5. (a) replaced hydrogen in dirigibles because it does not burn.

Content Words
a. helium
b. magnesium
c. hydrogen
d. potassium
e. phosphorus

STUDY HINT!

Try this experiment: say each list word, cover it, write it, then finally check to see if you spelled it right.

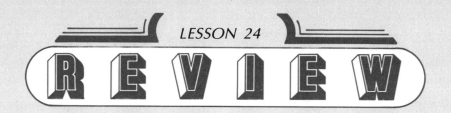

REVIEW

Steps to Help You Study Your Words

Before you write each word:
  Look at the word.
  Look at the letters.
  Say the word.
  Listen to the sounds.
When you write each word:
  Copy the word from your list.
  Remember how the word is spelled
    and write it.
After you write each word:
  Check the word with your list.
  Do you see any mistakes?
  Notice where the mistakes are and
    begin the steps again.

Study the review words. *(Lesson 19)*
part-time   fiberglass
close-up   all right*
doorknob   teammate*
Copy them, noting trouble spots.

_____

Choose two personal list words you
need to master. Copy them carefully.

Study the review words. *(Lesson 20)*
usage   cemetery
evaporate   itinerary*
anniversary   mileage*
Copy them, noting trouble spots.

_____

Choose two personal list words you
need to master. Copy them carefully.

Study the review words. *(Lesson 21)*
appreciation   squirrels
commotion   parallel*
professional   sheriff*
Copy them, noting trouble spots.

_____

Choose two personal list words you
need to master. Copy them carefully.

Study the review words. *(Lesson 22)*
autograph   static
democracy   atheist*
thermometer   epidemic*
Copy them, noting trouble spots.

_____

Choose two personal list words you
need to master. Copy them carefully.

Study the review words. *(Lesson 23)*
laboratory   vacuum
microscope   neutrons*
radioactive   photosynthesis*
Copy them, noting trouble spots.

_____

Choose two personal list words you
need to master. Copy them carefully.

Work with Review Words

1. Write the eleven review words with double consonants.
2. From the remaining words, write a review word that starts with each of the letters in this word: PNEUMATIC.
3. Print the remaining ten review words, leaving a blank space for all vowels. Then fill in the blanks and write the words.

Work with Personal Words

1. Alphabetize your ten personal words.
2. Select some of your personal words and arrange them on a grid, one below the other, so that the name of a food appears as you read down. For example:

```
M A T T E R
  T O R S I O N
S T R A N G L E
A S S U M E
U T T E R
```

Test Yourself

1. One compound word in each sentence below is improperly written. Write that compound correctly.
   a. It's alright if I take a part-time job.
   b. She took a close-up shot of my teamate.
   c. He bought a door-knob for the fiberglass door.
2. Match a word part from the first column with a word part from the second column to form a review word.

   a. mile   meter
   b. auto   synthesis
   c. demo   age
   d. thermo   graph
   e. micro   active
   f. radio   cracy
   g. photo   scope

3. Find the misspelled word in each group of words and write it correctly.
   a. parttime, squirrels, usage
   b. democracy, neutrons, statick
   c. epademic, sheriff, teammate
   d. commotion, fibreglass, cemetery
   e. parallel, vacuum, atheiste
   f. thermometer, labratory, anniversary
   g. evaporate, autograph, closup
   h. vacume, doorknob, itinerary

FROM AARDVARK TO ZERO

Part A

Say the words in the list below. Write the words.

1. albatross
2. alfalfa
3. almanac
4. apricot
5. gazelle
6. tariff
7. zero
8. accordion
9. dandruff
10. diesel
11. freckles
12. geyser
13. nickel
14. slalom
15. sleuth
16. thrive
17. wicker
18. yacht
19. aardvark *
20. dachshund *

The Germanic languages, which include Swedish, German, and Dutch, have contributed such list words to English as *nickel, accordion,* and *geyser.* And Arabic has contributed such list words as *almanac, apricot,* and *zero.*

● Write the list word, derived from the Arabic word *sifr,* that means "the absence of quantity."

● Write the list word, taken from the Swedish word *koppar-nickel,* that means "the metal niccolite."

∗Wild Words   That strange word with two **a**'s, *aardvark,* comes from Afrikaans, a Dutch dialect of South Africa. Literally, it means "earth pig."   The *dachshund* was originally bred to burrow down badger holes and flush out the animal for hunters. The word comes from the German *Dachs* ("badger") + *hund* ("dog").

Test Score:＿＿＿ —20   **92**   Part A Score:＿＿＿ —2

Part B

1. Read the Arabic word in the first column and its Arabic meaning in the second. Then write the English list word that is derived from the Arabic word.

   a. *al + ghattās*   "the sea eagle"
   b. *al + fasfas*   "the best fodder"
   c. *ta'rīf*   "list of taxes on goods"
   d. *ghazāl*   "an antelope"
   e. *al + barqūq*   "orange-colored fruit"
   f. *sifr*   "empty, nothing"
   g. *al + manākh*   "calendar"

2. Read the word derived from a Germanic language in the first column and its meaning in that language in the second. Then write the English list word that is derived from the Germanic word.

   a. *vikker* (Swedish)   "willow branch"
   b. *kopparnickel* (Swedish)   "the metal niccolite"
   c. *jaghtschip* (Dutch)   "chasing ship"
   d. *thrīfask* (Icelandic)   "take hold of"
   e. *geysa* (Icelandic)   "to gush"
   f. *slōth* (Icelandic)   "a trail"
   g. *freknur* (Icelandic)   "spots" or "spotty"
   h. *slalom* (Norwegian)   "zigzag ski race"
   i. *aarde + varken* (Afrikaans)   "earth" + "pig"
   j. *Diesel* (German)   the name of a German engineer and inventor
   k. *Akkordion* (German)   "a musical instrument"
   l. *Dachs + hund* (German)   "badger" + "dog"

3. The origin of one of the list words is uncertain. It means "scales of dead skin which flake off the scalp." Write the word.

WHAT'S THE BIG IDEA?

There is no easy way to remember the spellings of these words. The best idea is to memorize them.

DICTIONARY

Doublets are words that have different spellings but related meanings. Doublets can also be traced directly back to a single source word, as these sample etymologies show:

ci pher . . . . [< Medieval Latin *ciphra* < Arabic *sifr* empty. Doublet of ZERO.]
zer o . . . . [< Italian < Arabic *sifr* empty. Doublet of CIPHER.]

Though the word *cipher* came to English through Medieval Latin, and the word *zero* came to English through Italian, both words can be traced back to the Arabic word *sifr*.

Match the letters of the pairs of doublets in the second column with the source words for those doublets in the first column.

1. *fragilis*   a. lobster—locust
2. *caput*   b. money—mint
3. *moneta*   c. fragile—frail
4. *locusta*   d. chef—chief

Look up each word in the glossary and write its doublet.

5. regal   6. disk   7. cloak

An analogy is a comparison of one thing to another. Try your hand at these analogies by supplying the correct list word for the blank in each sentence.

1. Sedan is to car as ___ is to boat.
2. Beef is to meat as ___ is to fruit.
3. Polka dots are to material as ___ are to skin.
4. Hurdles are to running as ___ is to skiing.
5. Pound is to weight as ___ is to money.
6. Cotton is to fabric as ___ is to musical instrument.
7. Cougar is to cat as ___ is to antelope.
8. Tulip is to flower as ___ is to hay.

Part D

Choose the list or lists of words you want to learn this week. Then complete the activities next to each list you choose.

Review Words

1. Write the three review words, in alphabetical order, that begin with **s.**
2. Write the word with the double consonant.
3. What letter spells the sound /ə/ in (rel′ə tiv)? Write the word.

associate
relative
servant
sponsor
sergeant

Big Idea Words

1. Use the pronunciation symbols to write these words.
   a. A device for breathing under water is a (snôr′kəl).
   b. A (strü′dl) is a pastry filled with fruit or cheese.
   c. Moslems worship in a building called a (mosk).
   d. A glazed, salted, hard biscuit is a (pret′səl).
   e. A hot, dry wind, the (sə rok′ō), blows over Africa.
2. *Snorkel* comes from the German word meaning "nose." Write the list word that comes from the German word *Akkordion.*

mosque
pretzel
snorkel
strudel
sirocco

Challenge Words

Using the pronunciation symbols in parentheses, write the correct form of "good-by" in the languages below.

As in English, there are many ways to say "good-by" in other languages. For example, the French word (ə dü′) (1) simply means "good-by," but the French words (bôN vwä-yàzh′) (2) can mean "good-by," "good luck," or "pleasant trip." Both the German (ouf vē′dər zā′ən) (3) and the French (ō rə vwàr′) (4) mean "till we see each other again." And the Hawaiian word (ə lō′ə) (5) can mean "hello" or "good-by."

aloha
auf Wiedersehen
au revoir
adieu
bon voyage

⟨ STUDY HINT! ⟩

Study your list words by dividing them into groups—those derived from Arabic and those from Germanic languages.

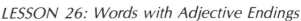

What's Characteristic?

Part A

Say the words in the list below. Write the words.

1. essential
2. social
3. fundamental
4. occasional
5. optional
6. vocational
7. characteristic
8. realistic
9. fantastic
10. magnetic
11. specific
12. terrific
13. ambitious
14. fictitious
15. mysterious
16. courageous
17. mischievous
18. nervous
19. athletic *
20. conscientious *

The words in this lesson have two things in common. All of them are used as adjectives, and all of them are related in meaning to some noun or verb.

- Write the list word that is related in meaning to the noun *essence*.
- Write the list word that is related in meaning to the noun *vocation*.
- Write the list word that is related in meaning to the verb *specify*.
- Write the list word that is related in meaning to the noun *fiction*.

*Wild Words   If you pronounce (ath let′ik) correctly, you should be able to spell it correctly.   Notice that /sh/ appears twice in *conscientious* (kon′shē en′shəs) and is spelled in two different ways.

Test Score:_____ —20   **96**   Part A Score:_____ —4

Part B

1. Write the list word that ends in **eous.**

2. Write the four list words that end in **ious.**

3. Write the two other list words that end in **ous.**

4. Write the two list words that end in **ial.**

5. Write the four other list words that end in **al.**

6. Write the two list words that end in **istic.**

7. Write the five other list words that end in **ic.**

8. Complete each item below by writing the list word that is related in meaning to the word that is underlined.

   a. Tom has never felt at ease in <u>society</u>. But in his new job he has to attend many _____ gatherings.

   b. Most stories of <u>fantasy</u> are not very convincing. It takes a good writer to make the _____ seem real.

   c. Why should your <u>conscience</u> bother you now? You never were that _____ before.

   d. The party next Friday is no big <u>occasion</u>. We just like to have _____ get-togethers with our friends.

9. Some adjectives put stress on the same syllable as the noun or verb they are related to (vo**ca**tion, vo**ca**tional); in other adjectives, the stress is on a different syllable (**mag**net, mag**net**ic).

   Pronounce the following pairs of words. Then write the three list words that stress a different syllable than the noun or verb they are related to.

terrify—terrific   mischief—mischievous   option—optional
athlete—athletic   courage—courageous

WHAT'S THE BIG IDEA?

Adjectives that are formed from or are related in meaning to nouns or verbs often end in **al, ic,** or **ous.**

Part C
Proofreading

Do you write the **ny** and **my** letter combinations clearly? Practice by writing these words.

testimony   *penny*   *mystery*

myself   *company*   *anything*

astronomy   *mummy*

Rewrite the sentences below, correcting the misspelled word in each. Remember to write **ny**'s and **my**'s clearly.

1. *It is essenchal that we all work in harmony.*
2. *Many fictitious characters are very relistic.*
3. *The mysterious look on her face made me nerveous.*
4. *Sammy is both ambitious and consceintious.*
5. *They kept denying that the fee was opshanal.*

&COMPANY

SPELLBOUND

Use the clues to supply these words ending with **ial.** Two of the words are list words.

1			i	a	l
	2		i	a	l
		3	i	a	l
		4	i	a	l
	5		i	a	l
6			i	a	l

1. knob that tunes in a radio or television
2. a hearing in court
3. liking to be with people
4. particular; unique
5. what a thing is made from
6. necessary; important

Part D

Choose the list or lists of words you want to learn this week.
Then complete the activities next to each list you choose.

1. Write the word that is related in meaning to
   a. Olympia   b. prosper   c. continent
2. The Latin word *superficies* means "surface." Which word
   means "on the surface; not thorough"?
3. Which word means "very active; full of energy"?
4. Write the list word that is related in meaning to the word
   nerve.

continental
Olympic
strenuous
superficial
prosperous

Challenge Words

1. The noun meaning "study of the mind" is *psychology,* and
   the adjective related to it is ____.
2. The noun meaning "treatment of diseases or disorders" is
   therapy, and the adjective related to it is ____.
3. The verb meaning "revive; bring back to life" is *resuscitate,* and the noun related to it is ____.
4. If *laryngitis* means "inflammation of the voice box," then
   the word for "voice box" is ____.
5. The tough, elastic substance that portions of the body skeleton, like the ear, are made of is called ____.

resuscitation
therapeutic
cartilage
psychological
larynx

Content Words

1. If you estimate the <u>value</u> of something, you do an ____.
2. If you estimate the <u>likelihood</u> that something will happen,
   you figure its ____.
3. Two words that in math mean "act of adding, subtracting,
   multiplying, or dividing" are ____ and ____.
4. If you count up the results of a vote, you ____ them.

calculation
tally
computation
evaluation
probability

STUDY HINT!

Study your list words by grouping them according to their
final letters: **al, ic,** or **ous.**

Seize a Suffix

Part A

Say the words in the list below. Write the words.

1. appreciative
2. detective
3. executive
4. possessive
5. progressive
6. restrictive
7. selective
8. comedian
9. custodian
10. librarian
11. physician
12. politician
13. creature
14. erasure
15. legislature
16. moisture
17. pressure
18. architecture
19. descriptive *
20. seizure *

All the words in this lesson end in *-ian, -ive,* or *-ure.* Sometimes these suffixes can simply be added to the root word to form a new word, as in *moist—moisture.* But often the final letter of the root word must be dropped before the suffix can be added.

● What happens to *appreciate* and *execute* when the suffix *-ive* is added to them?
● What happens to *comedy, custody,* and *library* when the suffix *-ian* is added to them?
● Underline the ending *-ive, -ian,* or *-ure* in the list words.

∗Wild Words   When adding *-ive* to *describe,* remember that the **be** in *describe* becomes **pt** in *descriptive.*

    If you can remember that /ē/ is spelled **ei** in *seizure,* then you should have no trouble spelling that word.

Part B

1. Add the suffix *-ive* to the following words.
   a. possess   b. restrict   c. select
   d. appreciate   e. execute   f. progress
   g. detect   h. describe
2. Add the suffix *-ian* to the following words.
   a. custody   b. physic   c. politic
   d. comedy   e. library
3. Add the suffix *-ure* to the following words.
   a. seize   b. architect   c. press
   d. moist   e. create   f. legislate
   g. erase

4. Rewrite each of the lettered words in the sentences below,
   correctly supplying the missing letters.

   The (a) lib_____an gave me a scary (b) de____tive
   story to read.

   If you want to know about the (c) ar____te____re
   of the building, try asking the (d) cus_____an.

   The (e) pol_____ian made an (f) ap_____ative
   speech before the (g) legi_____re.

   An (h) ex____tive often works under (i) pre____re.

   The (j) pr____essive (k) p_____ian developed a
   new method for dealing with an epileptic (l) s____ure.

WHAT'S THE BIG IDEA?

Sometimes the final **e** or **y** of a root word is dropped when
the suffix *-ive, -ian,* or *-ure* is added to it.

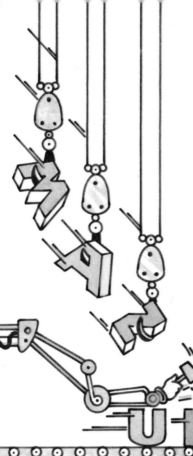

Dictionary

Many words have more than one meaning and can also be used as different parts of speech. For this reason, a dictionary will indicate the parts of speech a word may be used as and the meaning for the word when used as that part of speech. Notice in the sample entry below that the word *pressure* can be used as a noun *(n.)* or as a verb *(v.):*

pres sure (presh′ər), *n., v., . . .—n.* the continued action of a weight or force: *The pressure of the wind filled the sails of the boat.* —*v.* force or urge by exerting pressure: *The sales representative tried to pressure my parents into buying the encyclopedias.*

1. What does *pressure* mean when it is used as a noun?
2. What does *pressure* mean when it is used as a verb?
3. Look up the words below in the glossary. Write the parts of speech each word can be used as.
   a. manufacture   b. possessive
   c. progressive   d. detective

Being a librarian involves more than putting books on shelves. Here is what one librarian says about the importance of spelling in doing her job:

"The nature of a librarian's work is the organization and classification of information. I need a system for retrieving that information when people have questions that need answers. Because almost everything in the library is organized by the alphabet, I have to spell well to look things up and to relay information accurately. I also need spelling skills when I'm writing letters to publishers and film distributors, and when I write entry cards and summaries for books in the card catalog. If a name or fact is misspelled, it's likely I'll never find it again."

Choose the list or lists of words you want to learn this week.
Then complete the activities next to each list you choose.

Complete these sentences with the correct review word.

Review Words

they're
it's
safety
beauty
ninety

1. I think ____ supposed to rain today.
2. Over ____ golfers entered the tournament.
3. Seat belts are standard ____ features in cars.
4. Those rings were my grandmother's; ____ not for sale.
5. We stopped to admire the ____ of the mountain lake.

Big Idea Words

stature
passive
pedestrian
electrician
creative

1. Write the word formed from: a. create   b. electric
2. The Latin word *pedester* means "on foot." Which word means "person who goes on foot"?
3. Which word is the opposite of *active?*
4. Which word means "natural height of a person"?
5. Write the list word that is formed from *select.*

Write the content word that has the same letter as the letter in the blank in each sentence.

Content Words

a. subjunctive
b. exclamatory
c. declarative
d. reflexive
e. interrogative

1. A _(c)_ sentence states a fact, such as "She saw you."
2. An _(e)_ sentence asks a question, such as "Am I late?"
3. An _(b)_ sentence expresses strong feeling, such as "How tired we were!"
4. The _(a)_ mood of the verb is used in constructions like "If he **were** a year younger, he could get in free," because the idea expressed is contrary to fact.
5. The pronoun *herself* in the sentence "She cut herself" is _(d)_ because it reflects the action of the verb back onto the subject.

Write five original sentences using these constructions.

⨌TUDY HINT!

Study your list words by first grouping them according to their suffixes, then concentrating on each word in a group.

Your Number's Up!

Part A

Say the words in the list below. Write the words.

1. *monopoly*
2. *monotonous*
3. *unify*
4. *union*
5. *unison*
6. *unit*
7. *universe*
8. *university*
9. *bicycle*
10. *binoculars*
11. *triplets*
12. *tripod*
13. *quadrangle*
14. *pentagon*
15. *octagon*
16. *octave*
17. *decade*
18. *centigrade*
19. *bilingual* *
20. *decalogue* *

The words in this lesson contain Greek and Latin prefixes (such as *uni-* and *mono-*) as well as combining forms (such as *deca-* and *penta-*). Combining forms are forms of words that can be added to other words or other combining forms to make new words.

The prefix *bi-* means "two."
- Write the list word that means "a lightweight vehicle consisting of a metal frame with two wheels."

The combining form *deca-* means "ten."
- Write the list word that means "period of ten years."

✳Wild Words   A person who is *bilingual* speaks a second language as well or almost as well as his or her own language.

A *decalogue* is a set of ten rules. Remember that this word ends in **ue**!

Part B

Read the origins and meanings of the prefixes and combining forms below. Then use the definitions given in the following exercise to identify and write the list words. Check your glossary if you need additional help.

mono- [< Greek: single]
uni- [< Latin: one]
bi- [< Latin: twice]
bin- [< Latin: two by two]
tri- [< Latin or Greek: three]

quadr- [< Latin: four]
penta- [< Greek: five]
octa- [< Greek and Latin: eight]
deca- [< Greek: ten]
centi- [< Latin: hundred]

1. different sounds having one pitch
2. one institution made up of many schools
3. make or form into one
4. single ownership
5. groups of three
6. figure with eight sides and eight angles
7. four-sided enclosure surrounded by buildings
8. continuing in a single unvarying tone
9. period of ten years
10. group of eight
11. vehicle with two wheels
12. a three-legged support for a camera
13. temperature scale with an interval of 100° between the freezing and boiling points of water
14. the joining of two things into one
15. a double (two-by-two) telescope
16. figure with five sides and five angles
17. set of ten rules
18. one thing or person
19. able to speak a second language very well
20. the whole of existing things

WHAT'S THE BIG IDEA?

Learning Greek and Latin word forms showing number can help you figure out the meanings of many English words.

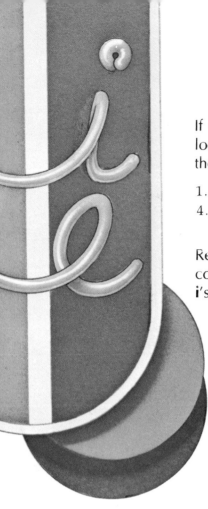

Proofreading

If you don't form the letters **i** and **e** clearly, the word *litter* may look like *letter*. Remember to loop the **e** and dot the **i.** Practice the letters by writing these words:

1. *universe*   2. *pentagon*   3. *bicycle*
4. *union*   5. *unify*   6. *triplets*

Read the following sentences. Then rewrite each sentence, correctly spelling any misspelled list words. Remember to form **i**'s and **e**'s carefully.

1. *Each year the univercity choir sings on the quadrangel.*
2. *If I use binokulers, I can see every expression on the director's face.*
3. *When the choir members sing in unason, the music is monotanus.*

Find the misspelled word in this sign and write the word correctly.

APPLICATIONS ACCEPTED FOR
CASHIER
FULL TIME HOURS – BENIFITS

Part D

hat, āge, fär;
let, ēqual, tėrm;
it, īce; hot, ōpen, ôrder;
oil, out; cup, pùt, rüle;
ch, child; ng, long; sh, she;
th, thin; ŦH, then;
zh, measure;

ə represents *a* in about,
e in taken, *i* in pencil,
o in lemon, *u* in circus.

Choose the list or lists of words you want to learn this week. Then complete the activities next to each list you choose.

Supply the missing letters; then write the review words.

Review Words

1. g___r__nt__
2. g___rd
3. p__s__n
4. p___v__le___
5. r_____ber

remember
privilege
guarantee
guard
prison

---

1. Write the word that contains *bi-* and means "twice a year."
2. Write the word that contains *centi-* and comes from Latin words meaning "hundred foot."
3. Write the word that contains *penta-* and means "line of verse having five metrical feet."
4. *Hexa-* means "six." Which word means "a plane figure having six angles and six sides"?
5. *Semi-* can mean "twice." Which word means "twice a month"?
6. Write the list word that contains *centi-*.

Big Idea Words

biannually
semimonthly
centipede
hexagon
pentameter

Use both the pronunciations and the definitions to help you write the correct challenge words.

Challenge Words

1. (ad hē′siv): a gummed tape used to hold bandages
2. (krōm): a metal that does not rust or become dull
3. (as bes′təs): a mineral that does not burn
4. (sel′yə lōs): substance used to make paper
5. (thėr′mō plas′tik): becoming soft and capable of being molded when heated

chrome
asbestos
thermoplastic
cellulose
adhesive

STUDY HINT!

In order to study the list words, group them according to their number prefixes or combining forms.

Preview the Arts

Part A

Say the words in the list below. Write the words.

1. ballet
2. chorus
3. cinema
4. dramatics
5. gallery
6. masterpiece
7. musician
8. orchestra
9. pantomime
10. performance
11. premiere
12. rehearsal
13. review
14. scenery
15. sculpture
16. soprano
17. symphony
18. theater
19. choreography *
20. ensemble *

The words in this list are good ones to use when you are writing about the fine arts—music, drama, dance, sculpture, and painting. For instance, if you were writing about music, you might use the words *musician* and *orchestra.* If you were writing about drama, you might use *theater* and *scenery.* And if you were writing about dancing, you might use *ballet* and *choreography.*

● Write the word that means "a person skilled in music."
● Write the word that means "place where plays are acted."

*Wild Words *Choreography,* the art of designing dances, is derived from the Greek word *choreia* ("dance") + *graphy* ("process of describing").   An *ensemble* is any harmonious group, but is usually a group of musicians or other performers.

Test Score:_____ —20   **108**   Part A Score:_____ —2

Part B

Read the sentences for each group of words below. Then complete each sentence with the correct word or words.

ballet   rehearsal   ensemble   choreography
1. The _(a)_ in *Rodeo,* a _(b)_ by Aaron Copland, is a spirited rendition of Western-style dancing.
2. Their first ____ was for going over act 2, scene 1.
3. After the final curtain, the entire ____ of performers met backstage for a party.

dramatics   pantomime   premiere   theater
4. Last week I saw a play in the school's ____.
5. Because I liked the play, I want to join the ____ club.
6. Part of acting is learning to express oneself without words but through gestures—the art of ____.
7. My ____ as an actor flopped—I forgot all my lines!

masterpiece   scenery   gallery   sculpture
8. The first ____ in the museum contained jewelry.
9. One ring we saw was a ____ of gold inlay.
10. Some ____, carved from granite, showed Indian gods.
11. The ____ painted on some jars depicted lush farmlands.

symphony   performance   orchestra   musician
12. My sister, a ____, plays first violin.
13. Her first public ____ was in a string quartet.
14. Right now, she is rehearsing for Mahler's First ____.
15. After college she hopes to join the Dalton Civic ____.

chorus   cinema   soprano   review
16. Her beautiful _(a)_ voice was so good she was asked to join the main _(b)_ of the opera company.
17. We went to the _(a)_ to see *Godzilla* because the _(b)_ we read in the paper said it was a good film.

WHAT'S THE BIG IDEA?

Memorize the spellings of your list words so you can more easily write about the arts you enjoy.

Dictionary

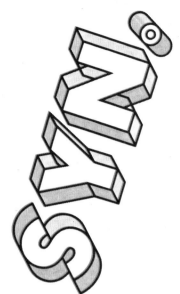

Using synonyms is one way to make your writing more accurate and more effective. But beware! Synonyms are not always interchangeable. While a particular synonym may be appropriate in one context, it may not work at all in another. In addition to a word's definitions, many dictionaries also give synonym studies for certain words:

last (last), *adj.* coming after all others; being at the end; final: *the last page of the book.* See synonym study below. **Syn.** *adj.* **Last, final, ultimate** mean coming after all others. **Last** applies to that which comes after all others in a series but is not necessarily the end of the series: *The last person to leave should turn off the light.* **Final** emphasizes the definite end of a series: *June 7 is the final day of classes for graduating seniors.* **Ultimate** emphasizes the last that can ever be reached or found: *Her ultimate goal was to become a dentist.*

1. What two words are given as synonyms for *last?*
2. Complete the following sentences with the correct word: *last, final,* or *ultimate.*
   a. Portillo struck out. He was the ____ man to bat in the inning.
   b. They never stopped to consider the ____ results of their actions.
   c. The play closes on March 17. The ____ performance will be at 8:00 P.M.
3. Write a sentence for each word.

The words below are clues to or parts of list words. Use the clues and parts to write the correct list word.

Example: ball, let   *Answer:* ballet

1. ant, pant, Tom
2. form, man
3. ear, hear
4. ram, mat, tic

5. ore, rap, chore
6. pie, aster, mast
7. eat, ate, heat

Part D

Choose the list or lists of words you want to learn this week. Then complete the activities next to each list you choose.

Review Words

1. Write the review words given in pronunciation symbols in this sentence:
   Of (kôrs) __(a)__ she's the (prin′sə pəl) __(b)__ of our (skül) __(c)__ ; in fact, (īm) __(d)__ certain of it.
2. In which two words must you capitalize the **i?**

Indian
course
school
I'm
principal

Challenge Words

Write the challenge word that has the same letter as the letter in the blank in each sentence.
1. An __(c)__ can bring water from a great distance.
2. A sluggish, marshy inlet of a lake is a __(e)__ .
3. Water can be stored underground in a __(b)__ .
4. A bay of water bordered by steep cliffs is a __(a)__ .
5. Frogs are common animals found in a __(d)__ .

a. fiord
b. cistern
c. aqueduct
d. lagoon
e. bayou

Content Words

Use the pronunciation symbols in parentheses to write the correct content words in this paragraph.

   The (fil′här mon′ik) __(1)__ orchestra gave an outstanding performance. They opened with a rousing (ō′vər chùr) __(2)__ . Next the percussion section was featured in a selection that had an unusual beat marked by (sing′kə pā′shən) __(3)__ . This was followed by the ensemble singing a simple (kə ral′) __(4)__ with a dramatic (kō′də) __(5)__ at the end.

syncopation
overture
chorale
coda
philharmonic

ʃTUDY HINT!

Study your list words by spelling each word aloud and then writing the word.

REVIEW

Steps to Help You Study Your Words

Before you write each word:
   Look at the word.
   Look at the letters.
   Say the word.
   Listen to the sounds.
When you write each word:
   Copy the word from your list.
   Remember how the word is spelled
     and write it.
After you write each word:
   Check the word with your list.
   Do you see any mistakes?
   Notice where the mistakes are and
     begin the steps again.

Study the review words. *(Lesson 25)*

dandruff	thrive
diesel	aardvark*
freckles	dachshund*

Copy them, noting trouble spots.

_____

Choose two personal list words you
need to master. Copy them carefully.

Study the review words. *(Lesson 26)*

occasional	mischievous
realistic	athletic*
terrific	conscientious*

Copy them, noting trouble spots.

_____

Choose two personal list words you
need to master. Copy them carefully.

Study the review words. *(Lesson 27)*

possessive	pressure
librarian	descriptive*
physician	seizure*

Copy them, noting trouble spots.

_____

Choose two personal list words you
need to master. Copy them carefully.

Study the review words. *(Lesson 28)*

university	centigrade
tripod	bilingual*
quadrangle	decalogue*

Copy them, noting trouble spots.

_____

Choose two personal list words you
need to master. Copy them carefully.

Study the review words. *(Lesson 29)*

orchestra	theater
performance	choreography*
scenery	ensemble*

Copy them, noting trouble spots.

_____

Choose two personal list words you
need to master. Copy them carefully.

Work with Review Words

1. Write all the review words in alphabetical order.
2. Write the five review words with double consonants.
3. Print the ten wild words plus five more review words, leaving spaces for all the vowels in each word. Then write the words, supplying the missing letters.

Work with Personal Words

1. List your ten personal words from the most difficult to the least difficult for you.
2. Make a word search puzzle in which at least five of your personal list words appear. Remember that words may appear across, down, on a diagonal, up, or even backwards. Use the puzzle at the right as a guide.

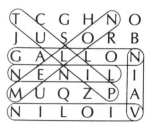

Test Yourself

1. In each sentence below you are given the base form of a review word in parentheses. Read each sentence; then write the correct form of the review word.
   a. That painting is a (real) depiction of the battle.
   b. My brother has a rather (possess) nature.
   c. The (library) pointed out the reference section.
   d. I put fifty pounds of (press) in the tires.
   e. Most of the (scene) maintained the gloomy mood.
   f. Their moving (perform) brought tears of triumph.
   g. Her story about the kibbutz was very (describe).

2. Match the numerical prefix in the first column with a word part in the second column to form a review word.
   a. tri-   versity
   b. deca-   grade
   c. quadr-   pod
   d. uni-   logue
   e. bi-   angle
   f. centi-   lingual

3. Find the correct spelling for each word and write it.
   a. mischievous, mischievious, mischivous
   b. athaletic, athletick, athletic
   c. phisician, physition, physician

113

Part A

Say the words in the list below. Write the words.

1. accessories
2. cabinet
3. chimney
4. corduroy
5. critical
6. dangerous
7. formerly
8. identify
9. interesting
10. literature
11. modern
12. poem
13. postponed
14. realize
15. recognized
16. similarity
17. strength
18. temperament
19. particularly *
20. sort of *

A few words in this lesson cause spelling problems because people generally mispronounce them: they add, change, or omit sounds when they say the words. Most of the others, however, cause problems because in normal speech they are pronounced slightly differently than they are spelled.

● Although in normal speech the word is often pronounced (in′tres ting), its correct spelling is ____.
● Although in normal speech the word is often pronounced (pōs pōnd′), its correct spelling is ____.
● Although in normal speech the word is often pronounced (tem′pər mənt), its correct spelling is ____.

∗Wild Words   *Particularly* is often misspelled because it is often mispronounced. Be sure to say and spell all five syllables of *par-tic-u-lar-ly*.   *Sort of* often does sound like "sorta," but it is spelled as two separate words.

*Test Score:*_____ —20   **114**   *Part A Score:*_____ —3

Part B

1. On each line below two possible pronunciations of a list word are given. After checking your glossary, write the letter of the correct pronunciation. Then write the word.

   a. (mod′ərn)   b. (mod′rən)
   c. (strengkth)   d. (strenth)
   e. (pər tik′yər lē)   f. (pər tik′yə lər lē)
   g. (rek′ä nīzd)   h. (rek′əg nīzd)
   i. (chim′nē)   j. (chim′ə nē)
   k. (for′mə lē)   l. (fôr′mər lē)

2. Rewrite each of the lettered words in the sentences below, correctly supplying the missing letters.

   Sue bought (a) ＿＿＿＿es＿ories for her
   (b) c＿＿d＿r＿y suit.

   Don't they (c) r＿＿l＿ze that their (d) chim＿＿y is falling apart?

   The delivery date for our new (e) cab＿net had been
   (f) pos＿po＿＿d for a week.

   Mr. Jansen finally (g) rec＿＿nized that his fiery
   (h) temp＿＿＿ment can (i) s＿＿t ＿f frighten people.

   Everyone was very (j) cr＿t＿c＿＿ of the (k) p＿＿m, but no one could (l) iden＿＿fy its author.

   (m) Form＿＿ly this intersection was very
   (n) dang＿r＿＿s.

   There is a (o) sim＿l＿r＿ty between the
   (p) lit＿r＿＿＿re books, but the new one is more
   (q) int＿＿＿＿ting.

WHAT'S THE BIG IDEA?

Many words are spelled slightly differently than the way they are usually pronounced in normal speech.

Part C

DICTIONARY

Many times in a dictionary entry you will find more than one pronunciation given for a word. Different pronunciations for the same word are called variant pronunciations.

Sometimes a word is pronounced differently when it is used as a different part of speech. For example, *record* is pronounced (rek′ərd) when it is used as a noun (He kept a *record* of his test grades) and (ri kôrd′) when it is used as a verb (Did anyone *record* the concert?).

However, variant pronunciations occur even when a word is used as only one part of speech. This is because as language grows and changes, the way that words are said sometimes changes too. When this changeover process takes a long time (as it usually does), it often happens that two or more pronunciations are in common use at the same time.

Use your glossary and determine the number of variant pronunciations that exist for each of the following words.

strength   interesting   literature   corduroy

SPELLBOUND

All your list words can be found vertically, horizontally, diagonally, forwards, or backwards in this puzzle.

```
l a g y l r e m r o f r e a l i z e
v e n d a n g e r o u s z o c t r i
d o i t c p o s t p o n e d e u m d
e r t e m a l a b l v t q u t p s e
z a s m b c c a b i n e t a i j k n
i l e p a r t i c u l a r l y m n t
n o r e o p y q n i r e s t u v w i
g x e r y e z a b e t c s o r t o f
o i t a n j m k s i m i l a r i t y
c l n m m p n o l q r n r e d o m s
e t i e u v y o r u d r o c w o x z
r h y n a d c s e i r o s s e c c a
c e s t r e n g t h f i l g j m h k
```

Part D

Choose the list or lists of words you want to learn this week.
Then complete the activities next to each list you choose.

Complete these sentences with the correct review word.
1. If you _____ that key, we'll never get in the building.
2. Cy had to _____ between playing basketball and hockey.
3. He finally _____ basketball.
4. He had to _____ the fact that he needed more study time.
5. Nothing anyone says can _____ my decision.

Review Words
accept
affect
choose
chose
lose

1. Write these words, supplying the missing letters.
   a. pi___ting   b. cont_____   c. rad_a___r
   d. a_r_bat   e. card_____l
2. Write this list word: mod_____.

Big Idea Words
radiator
picketing
acrobat
cardinal
contact

Write the content word from mathematics that has the same
letter as the letter in the blank in each sentence.
1. Two lines that cross each other are said to _(e)_.
2. A _(d)_ number is one that can be reached by counting.
3. The _(b)_ principle says that you can add or multiply numbers in any order without changing the result.
4. The _(a)_ principle says that you can add or multiply numbers in any combination without changing the result.
5. The _(c)_ principle says that you get the same result whether you perform multiplication on a set of numbers or on
   each member of the set individually.
Tell which principle each of the following demonstrates:
1. $2+3=3+2$ 2. $2(5+4)=(2\times5)+(2\times4)$ 3. $(2+4)+5=2+(4+5)$

Content Words
a. associative
b. commutative
c. distributive
d. finite
e. intersect

ﬆUDY HINT!

Study your list words by looking at their spellings carefully and remembering to include each letter.

Memorable Endings

Part A

Say the words in the list below. Write the words.

1. breakable
2. comfortable
3. considerable
4. enjoyable
5. maneuverable
6. obtainable
7. memorable
8. imaginable
9. movable
10. reliable
11. collectible
12. convertible
13. indestructible
14. permissible
15. reducible
16. responsible
17. reversible
18. sensible
19. manageable *
20. noticeable *

All of your list words end in either *-able* or *-ible,* two adjective-forming suffixes. These suffixes have various meanings when added to base words. For example, *permit* + *-ible* means "that which can be permitted," *comfort* + *-able* means "giving or suitable for comfort," and *break* + *-able* means "liable to be broken."

● Write the list word that is formed when *-able* is added to *imagine.* What letter is dropped?
● Write the list word that is formed when *-ible* is added to *permit.* What happens to the letter **t?**
● Underline each *-able* and *-ible* in your list words.

✱Wild Words   You must keep the **e** in *manage* when you add *-able* in order to keep the sound /j/. You must also keep the **e** in *notice* when you add *-able* in order to keep the sound /s/.

*Test Score:*_____—20   **118**   *Part A Score:*_____—24

Part B

1. Write the list word that is formed by adding the suffix in the second column to the base word in the first. Pay close attention to any spelling changes that occur to the base word when the suffix is added.

Base Word		Suffix	
a. comfort	+	-able	=
b. break	+	-able	=
c. maneuver	+	-able	=
d. manage	+	-able	=
e. obtain	+	-able	=
f. enjoy	+	-able	=
g. convert	+	-ible	=
h. (in)destruct	+	-ible	=
i. memory	+	-able	=
j. imagine	+	-able	=
k. rely	+	-able	=
l. reverse	+	-ible	=
m. sense	+	-ible	=
n. permit	+	-ible	=

2. In which word did you change the final **t** to a double **s** before adding *-ible?*

3. You divide most words with suffixes before the suffix at the end of a writing line, though not all. Check these words in your glossary. Copy those words that are divided correctly. Be sure to include the hyphens.

a. mo-vable	e. notice-able	i. respon-sible
b. mov-able	f. notic-eable	j. respons-ible
c. consider-able	g. redu-cible	k. collect-ible
d. conside-rable	h. reduc-ible	l. collec-tible

WHAT'S THE BIG IDEA?

Because the suffixes *-able* and *-ible* sound similar, you will have to memorize the spelling of each list word.

Proofreading

Two of the more common uses of the colon (:) are:
- after the formal salutation in a letter, or after the introductory remark of a speaker making an address

    Dear Mrs. Brown: Ladies and Gentlemen:

- to introduce a list or series at the end of a sentence

    The documentary was on the following topics: solar energy, wind energy, and nuclear energy sources.

Hurrying to a luncheon, a guest speaker jotted down a few remarks, some of which are given below. Supply the two missing colons and rewrite the five misspelled words.

My dear colleagues

Many of my goals, I think, are not only sensble but also obtanable. My plans cover the following areas comfertible housing, a managable tax increase, and a noticable improvement in the community health care program.

Use the clues to supply these words ending in *-able*.

1		a	b	l	e	
2			a	b	l	e
3			a	b	l	e
4				a	b	l	e
5				a	b	l	e

1. can be moved
2. can be relied upon
3. worth remembering
4. can be imagined
5. giving comfort

Part D

Choose the list or lists of words you want to learn this week.
Then complete the activities next to each list you choose.

---

1. Write the review words that have double consonants.

2. Write the word with an **i** before **e.**

Review Words
approximately
experience
opportunity
exaggerate
parallel

---

1. Write the word that means
   a. that which can be used.
   b. that which can be marketed.
   c. that which can be collapsed.
   d. that which can be controlled.
2. Write the word that means "able to get along with."
3. Write the list word that means "that can be reversed."

Big Idea Words
controllable
usable
compatible
collapsible
marketable

Write the challenge word that has the same letter as the letter in the blank in each sentence.
1. The art of (c) means knowing how to use words well.
2. Hamlet's (a) which begins "To be or not to be" is one of the most famous in literature.
3. Skill and eloquence in speaking is known as (e) .
4. The comedian on the show gave a ten-minute (b) .
5. Clear pronunciation and effective hand gestures are parts of learning (d) .

Challenge Words
a. soliloquy
b. monologue
c. rhetoric
d. elocution
e. oratory

STUDY HINT!

Study your list words by grouping them according to whether they end in *-able* or in *-ible.*

What a Combination!

Part A

Say the words in the list below. Write the words.

1. aerial
2. aisle
3. amateur
4. cantaloupe
5. counterfeit
6. doesn't
7. gauge
8. greyhound
9. guinea
10. leopard
11. lieutenant
12. ought
13. pageant
14. sauerkraut
15. sergeant
16. slaughtered
17. sovereign
18. trousseau
19. bouillon *
20. Europe *

The words in this lesson each contain two or three vowels together. Since these vowel combinations are often holdover spelling patterns from the language that the word originated in, their spellings may be a little different from what you would expect.

- Which four list words have three vowels together?
- Which two list words have the two-vowel combination **eu?**
- Which two list words have the vowel combination **ei?**
- Underline all the vowel combinations in your list words.

✱Wild Words The vowel combinations in both *bouillon* (bül′yon) and *Europe* come from the languages the words originated in. *Bouillon,* which is a clear thin soup or broth, is derived from the French word *bouiller,* "to boil." *Europe* comes from *Europa,* the name of a princess who in Greek mythology was carried off by the god Zeus.

Test Score: _____ —20   **122**   Part A Score: _____ —34

Part B

1. Write the list word that has the vowel combination **oui.**

2. Write the five list words with the vowel combination **ou.**

3. Write the three list words with the vowel combination **au.**

4. Write the three list words with the vowel combination **ae.**

5. Write the list word with the vowel combination **ieu.**

6. Using the clues provided, supply the missing vowels and write the appropriate list words.

   a. __m__t____r: person who is not a professional
   b. g____g__: instrument for measuring
   c. c__nt__l____p__: a melon
   d. d____sn't: a contraction
   e. gr__yh____nd: a breed of dog
   f. s_____rkr____t: sour cabbage
   g. s__rg____nt: a noncommissioned military officer
   h. s__v__r____gn: supreme ruler, such as a king
   i. sl____ght__r__d: butchered
   j. ____r__p__: a continent
   k. ____sl__: passage between rows of seats
   l. ____r____l: an antenna
   m. c_____nt__rf____t: forged; not genuine
   n. g_____n____: type of pig or hen
   o. l____p__rd: fierce animal of the cat family
   p. ____ght: be obliged
   q. p__g_____nt: an elaborate spectacle
   r. l_____t__n__nt: a commissioned military officer

WHAT'S THE BIG IDEA?

Words that keep the spelling patterns of the language they originated in often have unusual vowel combinations.

Part B Score: _____ —31 **123**

Dictionary

Besides the dictionary, there are several other useful sources of information. These four are commonly used:

Encyclopedia — book or set of books containing articles on all branches of knowledge

Thesaurus — book listing synonyms and sometimes antonyms of words

Almanac — book published once a year containing recent information on many subjects

Atlas — book of maps

Which reference aid would contain the best information on each topic below? Write the word that is underlined in each topic under the name of the appropriate aid.

1. an antonym for aerial
2. the major seas of Europe
3. where a leopard can be found
4. the number of people slaughtered on our highways in 1973
5. the characteristics of a greyhound
6. the early life of Britain's sovereign, Elizabeth II
7. the British Amateur Golf Champion of 1976
8. synonyms for counterfeit

ENCYCLOPEDIA   THESAURUS   ALMANAC   ATLAS

SPELLBOUND

Using these letter values, figure out how much each of your list words is worth. Then answer the questions below.

1¢ letters	2¢ letters	3¢ letters	4¢ letters	5¢ letters
a,e,i,o,u,c,s,t	b,d,h,k,l,m,n,r	f,g,j,p,w	q,v,y	x,z

1. Which is the most expensive word in this lesson?
2. Which word costs a dime?
3. Which two words each cost thirteen cents?
4. Which three words each cost eight cents?

Part D

Choose the list or lists of words you want to learn this week.
Then complete the activities next to each list you choose.

---

1. Which word has a double consonant?
2. Which word has a double vowel?
3. Which two words contain three syllables?
4. Which word has one syllable?
5. Write a sentence using each word.

Review Words
skiing
athletic
incident
group
challenge

---

1. Write these words, supplying the missing vowels.
   a. c__ll___g__   b. fl___r__d__   c. __nt__nn___
   d. c___ss__n   e. h___rs__n__ss

2. Write the list word with the vowel combination **ai.**

Big Idea Words
fluoride
antennae
hoarseness
colleague
caisson

Write the content word that has the same letter as the letters
in the blanks in each sentence.
1. _(d)_ is an English game somewhat like football.
2. In _(e)_ physical exercises are usually performed with the
   aid of some kind of equipment; in _(c)_ little or no additional equipment is used.
3. _(b)_ is a system of exercises and positions derived from a
   Hindu religious philosophy.
4. _(a)_ involves strenuous exercises, such as running and
   swimming, that help increase the body's intake of oxygen.

What type of exercise is each item below an example of?
1. jogging   2. pushups   3. parallel bars

Content Words
a. aerobics
b. yoga
c. calisthenics
d. rugby
e. gymnastics

✎TUDY HINT!

Study your list words by paying particular attention to
the vowels and vowel combinations in each.

The Sound That's Hard to Hear

Part A

Say the words in the list below. Write the words.

1. suburban
2. metropolitan
3. strengthen
4. foreign
5. villain
6. gallon
7. familiar
8. particular
9. peculiar
10. behavior
11. minor
12. motor
13. professor
14. proper
15. tractor
16. tremendous
17. unanimous
18. citrus
19. hippopotamus *
20. siphon *

Did you notice that each of the list words ends in /ən/, /ər/, or /əs/? These sounds can be spelled a number of ways. The sound /ən/, for example, is spelled **an, en, eign, ain,** and **on** in the lesson. The sound /ər/ is spelled **er, ar,** and **or.** And the sound /əs/ is spelled **ous** and **us.**

● Write the letters that spell /ən/ in *foreign.* Write the word.
● Write the letters that spell /əs/ in *unanimous.* Write the word.
● Underline each spelling of the sound /ər/ that occurs in your list words.

*Wild Words   A *hippopotamus*—the word comes from the Greek words *hippos* ("horse") + *potamos* ("river")—is a massive amphibious mammal. A *siphon*—from the Greek word *siphōn* ("pipe")—is a bent tube used to draw off water.

Test Score: _____ —20   **126**   Part A Score: _____ —13

Part B

1. Write the letters that spell the sound /ən/ in these words; then write the entire word.

   a. suburb___ ___
   b. gall___ ___
   c. metropolit___ ___
   d. vill___ ___ ___
   e. strength___ ___
   f. for___ ___ ___ ___
   g. siph___ ___

2. Write the letters that spell the sound /əs/ in these words; then write the entire word.

   a. citr___ ___
   b. tremend___ ___ ___
   c. unanim___ ___ ___
   d. hippopotam___ ___

3. Write the letters that spell the sound /ər/ in these words; then write the entire word.

   a. famili___ ___
   b. tract___ ___ ___
   c. particul___ ___ ___
   d. profess___ ___ ___
   e. peculi___ ___ ___
   f. prop___ ___
   g. behavi___ ___ ___
   h. min___ ___ ___
   i. mot___ ___ ___

   j. In three of the words, what letter spells /y/ before /ər/?

WHAT'S THE BIG IDEA?

Notice that the sounds /ən/, /əs/, and /ər/ can be spelled in a number of ways.

Proofreading

hat, āge, fär;
let, ēqual, tėrm;
it, īce; hot, ōpen, ôrder;
oil, out; cup, pùt, rüle;
ch, child; ng, long; sh, she;
th, thin; ᴛʜ, then;
zh, measure;

ə represents *a* in about,
e in taken, *i* in pencil,
o in lemon, *u* in circus.

You know that the letter combinations **ar, er,** and **or** can all spell the sound /ər/. When you are writing words with these endings, you must make sure you form each combination clearly. Practice these letter combinations by identifying the following list words which are shown in pronunciation symbols. Then write each word, being careful to write the **ar, er,** and **or** combinations clearly.

1. (bi hā′vyər)
2. (prə fes′ər)
3. (pi kyü′lyər)
4. (prop′ər)
5. (mī′nər)
6. (trak′tər)
7. (pər tik′yə lər)
8. (mō′tər)
9. (fə mil′yər)

Read the following passage taken from a letter. Rewrite correctly the six misspelled list words, and pay close attention to writing any **ar, er,** and **or** combinations.

School starts in a month for me and I've already chosen my subjects. First, there'll be a foriegn language, probably French; then chemistry to strengthan my science background. I'm also going to take advanced algebra, which should prove to be a tremendus challenge. Finally, I'll take my particuler favorite, auto shop, since it's the most familyer to me and is also taught by my favorite professer.

SPELLBOUND

Find the incorrectly written word in this picture and rewrite it correctly.

WE'RE No.1
BURGLER ALARMS
438-2896   STAND GUARD

hat, āge, fär;
let, ēqual, tėrm;
it, īce; hot, ōpen, ôrder;
oil, out; cup, pùt, rüle;
ch, child; ng, long; sh, she;
th, thin; ᴛʜ, then;
zh, measure;

ə represents a in about,
e in taken, i in pencil,
o in lemon, u in circus.

Choose the list or lists of words you want to learn this week.
Then complete the activities next to each list you choose.

Big Idea Words

1. Write the words in which /ər/ is spelled **or.**
2. Write the words in which /ər/ is spelled **er.**
3. Write a list word and a word from the right in which /ər/ is spelled **ar.**
4. Write a list word and a word from the right that contain the sound /əs/.

illustrator
burglar
cruiser
folder
decorator

Challenge Words

Use the pronunciation symbols in parentheses to write the correct challenge words.
1. She had an (ə brā′zhən) on her knee from the fall.
2. Chemical (kə rō′zhən) turned the metal dish black.
3. The (kaz′əm) between those two has grown bigger.
4. It took weeks to clean the (də brē′) from the flood.
5. Rain caused the (dis in′tə grā′shən) of the rocks.

debris
corrosion
chasm
disintegration
abrasion

Content Words

Write the content word that has the same letter as the letter in the blank in each sentence.
1. The (d) glands are located near the kidneys.
2. (a) carries oxygen from the lungs to tissues.
3. An important (b) in the body is insulin.
4. The "master gland" in the human body is the (c) .
5. An improperly functioning (e) gland can cause a dangerous gain or loss of weight.

a. hemoglobin
b. hormone
c. pituitary
d. adrenal
e. thyroid

⌠TUDY HIΠT!

Study your list words by grouping them according to the sound of their endings: /ən/, /əs/, and /ər/.

How Do You Feel?

Part A

Say the words in the list below. Write the words.

1. anxiety
2. apathy
3. bewildered
4. boredom
5. compassion
6. confident
7. depressed
8. elated
9. empathy
10. enthusiastic
11. frustrated
12. grief
13. hatred
14. loneliness
15. relax
16. satisfaction
17. sympathetic
18. upset
19. jubilant *
20. melancholy *

This lesson presents some words that can be used to describe how people feel in various situations.

- Write the list word that means "weariness caused by dull, tiresome people or things."
- Write the list word that means "condition of being pleased and contented."
- Write the two list words that have to do with showing kind feelings, or sympathy, toward others.

✱Wild Words   *Jubilant* comes from a Latin word meaning "wild shout."   *Melancholy* has an interesting history. Once people believed that certain body fluids determined a person's health and disposition; too much black bile, for example, caused sadness and depression. The English word *melancholy* comes from Greek words meaning "black bile."

Part B

Complete each of the following passages with list words.

Jean, far from home, was __(1)__ by feelings of intense __(2)__. All she was looking for from the others in the dorm was some sympathy or __(3)__. But they acted indifferently, and it was that __(4)__ that hurt her the most.

upset
loneliness
apathy
compassion

The prospect of sheer __(5)__ for the summer months made George pretty __(6)__. He tried several places for work but without luck. Finally, he tried a small grocery store. The owner was __(7)__ to George's plight and offered him a job. George, feeling __(8)__, ran home with the news.

elated
sympathetic
boredom
depressed

When the main character, whose troubles were similar to my own, was captured, I felt great __(9)__ with him. His __(10)__ of the enemy glared in his eyes. Suffering and __(11)__ swelled in his mind over the loss of his crew. Now things were hopeless, and he became depressed and __(12)__.

melancholy
grief
hatred
empathy

Paco stared at the plans, a confused look on his face. He remained __(13)__ until Ms. Casas explained the project. Then Paco started to __(14)__. Soon he became excited and __(15)__. When the model was done, he felt a sense of __(16)__.

satisfaction
bewildered
enthusiastic
relax

Karen awaited the election results with some __(17)__. She was __(18)__ that she would make a good class president, but she still felt nervous about her chances of winning. As time passed, she grew more __(19)__ and impatient. Finally, the announcement came. Karen was __(20)__. She had won!

frustrated
jubilant
anxiety
confident

WHAT'S THE BIG IDEA?

Your emotions play an important role in your daily life, and you should know how to spell words to describe them.

Dictionary

Most words have more than one meaning, and the various meanings of many words can be found in a dictionary. The following is part of an entry that one dictionary has for the word *upset:*

up set (up set′), *v.* **1** tip over; overturn: *upset a boat.* **2** disturb greatly; disorder: *Rain upset our plans for the picnic. The shock upset his nerves.* **3** defeat unexpectedly in a contest: *The independent candidate upset the mayor in the election.*

Though there are several more definitions for *upset,* these three represent various meanings of the word. Did you also notice that each definition was followed by an example sentence or phrase? These are to help you understand the various meanings the word has so that you can use it correctly.

In each group of sentences below, the same word is used two different ways. First, read each sentence, and then check the italicized word in the glossary. Second, copy the word and write after it the definition number used.

1a. They are *confident* that he was telling the truth.
1b. He displayed a *confident* manner during the exams.
2a. *Relax* your arms and legs when you dance.
2b. They usually *relax* discipline on the last day of school.
3a. The French were *sympathetic* to the American cause.
3b. We felt *sympathetic* when we learned she was ill.
4a. The rain over the weekend made me *depressed.*
4b. She *depressed* the "start" button.
5a. Our inability to help left us feeling *frustrated.*
5b. The police *frustrated* the bandits' robbery attempt.

Complete the following sentences with the correct list word.
1. If happy becomes happiness then lonely becomes ___.
2. If king becomes kingdom then bore becomes ___.
3. If jump becomes jumped then bewilder becomes ___.
4. If apathy becomes apathetic then sympathy becomes ___.
5. If pious becomes piety then anxious becomes ___.

Part D

hat, āge, fär;
let, ēqual, tėrm;
it, īce; hot, ōpen, ôrder;
oil, out; cup, pùt, rüle;
ch, child; ng, long; sh, she;
th, thin; ŦH, then;
zh, measure;

ə represents *a* in about,
e in taken, *i* in pencil,
o in lemon, *u* in circus.

Choose the list or lists of words you want to learn this week.
Then complete the activities next to each list you choose.

Review Words

1. Write the words that spell the sound /j/ with a **g** and end with the sound /ē/.
2. Write the words that have two sets of double consonants.
3. Write the word with an **ie** combination.
4. Write a sentence using each of these words.

embarrass
cries
biology
aggressive
tragedy

Challenge Words

Use both the pronunciations and the definitions to help you write the correct challenge words.
1. (dev′ə stāt): "to lay waste; destroy"
2. (i vak′yü āt): "leave empty; withdraw from"
3. (ə nī′ə lāt): "to destroy completely"
4. (kat′ə kliz′əm): "any sudden, violent change in the earth"
5. (kə tas′trə fē): "a sudden, widespread, or extraordinary disaster"

catastrophe
devastate
cataclysm
evacuate
annihilate

Content Words

Complete each sentence with the correct content word.
1. A four-____ car can be very economical to run.
2. A funnel is made in the basic shape of a ____.
3. The room's ____ measured sixteen by ten feet.
4. A square is to plane geometry as a ____ is to solid geometry.
5. Circles drawn so that they interweave make a ____ design.

cone
geometric
cube
cylinder
dimensions

STUDY HINT!

Study your list words by saying each word aloud and then writing the word.

REVIEW

Steps to Help You Study Your Words

Before you write each word:
   Look at the word.
   Look at the letters.
   Say the word.
   Listen to the sounds.
When you write each word:
   Copy the word from your list.
   Remember how the word is spelled
      and write it.
After you write each word:
   Check the word with your list.
   Do you see any mistakes?
   Notice where the mistakes are and
      begin the steps again.

Study the review words. **(Lesson 31)**

cabinet	recognized
corduroy	particularly✱
identify	sort of✱

Copy them, noting trouble spots.

_____

Choose two personal list words you
need to master. Copy them carefully.

Study the review words. **(Lesson 32)**

maneuverable	sensible
movable	manageable✱
reliable	noticeable✱

Copy them, noting trouble spots.

_____

Choose two personal list words you
need to master. Copy them carefully.

Study the review words. **(Lesson 33)**

aerial	sergeant
lieutenant	bouillon✱
sauerkraut	Europe✱

Copy them, noting trouble spots.

_____

Choose two personal list words you
need to master. Copy them carefully.

Study the review words. **(Lesson 34)**

foreign	unanimous
villain	hippopotamus✱
familiar	siphon✱

Copy them, noting trouble spots.

_____

Choose two personal list words you
need to master. Copy them carefully.

Study the review words. **(Lesson 35)**

anxiety	loneliness
enthusiastic	jubilant✱
grief	melancholy✱

Copy them, noting trouble spots.

_____

Choose two personal list words you
need to master. Copy them carefully.

Work with Review Words

1. Write the five review words that end in **y.**
2. Write the seventeen review words that have two or more vowels together. Underline the vowel combinations. (Hint: The **y** in *corduroy* is not a vowel.)
3. Write a review word that starts with each of the letters in this word: JERUSALEM.

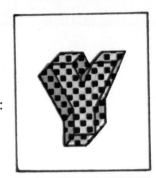

Work with Personal Words

1. Group your ten personal words according to the number of vowels each has. Put words with two vowels in one group, words with three vowels in another, and so on.
2. Make a crossword puzzle, using at least five of your personal words.

Test Yourself

Decide which underlined word, if any, is misspelled in the following sentences. Write the number of the misspelled word; then write the word correctly. If no word is misspelled, write the number 4.

1. It might be more ¹sensable to mix the ²bouillon in with the ³sauerkraut. ⁴None
2. Both the ¹sergeant and the ²lieutenant said that ³lonliness was the worst part of being stationed overseas. ⁴None
3. We were all ¹sorta pleased that no one could ²identify the ³villain. ⁴None
4. There was ¹unanimous agreement among the test drivers that the ²foreign car was the most ³maneuverable in traffic. ⁴None
5. As it grew more ¹familiar with its surroundings, the ²hippopatamus became more ³manageable. ⁴None
6. Neither Frank Adams nor his brother was ¹particularly ²enthusiastic about being ³recagnized in public by Dr. Lawlor. ⁴None
7. Her ¹anxiety turned to ²grief when she learned that even her grandmother's treasured antique ³cabenet had been stolen. ⁴None
8. This cutter is very ¹reliable; its most ²noticeable features are its three ³movable blades. ⁴None

135

Parts of a Dictionary Entry

① ②

④ de lib er ate (*adj.* di lib′ər it; *v.* di lib′ə- **③**
rāt′), *adj., v.,* **-at ed, -at ing.** —*adj.* ◄
carefully thought out beforehand; in- **⑥**
tended: *a deliberate lie.* See synonym
⑤ study below.—*v.i., v.t.* think over carefully; consider. [< Latin *deliberatum*
carefully weighed < *de-* + *librare* **⑦**
weigh] —**de lib′er ate ly,** *adv.* **⑧**
Syn. *adj.* **Deliberate, intentional**
mean done after thinking over. **Delib-**
erate suggests full thought before act- **⑨**
ing: *The lawyer made a deliberate at-*
tempt to confuse the jury. **Intentional**
means done on purpose: *His mean*
remark was intentional; he wanted to
make you angry.

① **Entry word**   ⑥ **Illustrative sentence**
② **Pronunciation**   ⑦ **Etymology**
③ **Part-of-speech label** ⑧ **Run-on entry**
④ **Inflected forms**   ⑨ **Synonym study**
⑤ **Definition**

Spellings of English Sounds*

SYMBOL: SPELLINGS:

a **at**, pl**ai**d, h**a**lf, l**au**gh
ā **a**ble, **ai**d, s**ay**, **a**ge, **eigh**t, th**ey**, br**ea**k,
   v**ei**n, g**au**ge, cr**e**pe, ber**et**
ä **fa**ther, **ah**, c**a**lm, h**ea**rt, baz**aa**r
b **b**ad, ra**bb**it
ch **ch**ild, wa**tch**, fu**t**ure, ques**t**ion
d **d**id, a**dd**, fille**d**
e **e**nd, s**ai**d, **ae**rial, **a**ny, br**ea**d, s**ay**s,
   h**ei**fer, l**eo**pard, fr**ie**nd, b**u**ry
ē **e**qual, **ea**t, **ee**l, happ**y**, cit**ie**s, c**ei**ling,
   rec**ei**ve, k**ey**, th**e**se, bel**ie**ve, mach**i**ne,
   l**i**ter, p**eo**ple
ėr st**er**n, **ear**th, **ur**ge, f**ir**st, w**or**d, j**our**ney,
   err, p**urr**
f **f**at, **ph**rase, e**ff**ort, lau**gh**
g **g**o, **g**uest, **gh**ost, e**gg**, leagu**e**
h **h**e, **wh**o, **j**ai alai

SYMBOL: SPELLINGS:

i **i**t, **E**ngland, **ear**, h**y**mn, b**ee**n, s**ie**ve,
   w**o**men, b**u**sy, b**ui**ld, w**ei**rd
ī **I**, **i**ce, l**ie**, sk**y**, t**y**pe, r**ye**, **eye**, **i**sland,
   h**igh**, **ei**der, **ai**sle, h**eigh**t, b**uy**, c**o**y**o**te
j **j**am, **g**em, exa**gg**erate, sche**d**ule, ba**dg**er,
   bri**dg**e, sol**d**ier, lar**g**e, alle**gi**ance
k **c**oat, **k**ind, **ch**aos, **q**uit, **kh**aki, ba**ck**,
   a**ch**e, a**cc**ount, anti**qu**e, ex**c**ite, a**cqu**ire
l **l**and, te**ll**
m **m**e, com**m**on, cli**mb**, sole**mn**, pal**m**
n **n**o, **kn**ife, **gn**aw, **pn**eumonia, ma**nn**er
ng lo**ng**, i**nk**, ha**n**dkerchief, to**ngue**
o **o**dd, w**a**tch, **ho**nest, **ya**cht
ō **o**pen, **oa**k, t**oe**, **ow**n, h**o**me, **oh**, f**o**lk,
   th**ough**, bur**eau**, s**ew**, br**oo**ch, s**ou**l
ô **o**rder, **a**ll, **au**thor, **aw**ful, b**oar**d,
   b**ough**t, w**a**lk, t**augh**t, c**ough**, Ut**a**h
oi **oi**l, b**oy**
ou **ou**t, **ow**l, b**ough**, h**ou**r
p **p**ay, ha**pp**y
r **r**un, ca**rr**y, **wr**ong, **rh**ythm
s **s**ay, **c**ent, **ps**ychology, **s**cent, **s**word,
   mi**ss**, dan**c**e, ten**s**e, pi**zz**a, li**s**ten
sh **sh**e, **ch**ef, **s**ure, **sch**wa, o**c**ean, spe**ci**al,
   ten**s**ion, mi**ss**ion, na**ti**on
t **t**ell, **tw**o, **Th**omas, **pt**omaine, bu**tt**on,
   stopp**ed**, dou**bt**, recei**pt**, pi**zz**a, pli**ght**
th **th**in
ᵀH **th**en, brea**the**
u **u**p, **o**ven, tr**ou**ble, d**oe**s, fl**oo**d
u̇ f**u**ll, g**oo**d, w**o**lf, sh**ou**ld
ü f**oo**d, j**u**nior, r**u**le, bl**ue**, **wh**o, m**o**ve,
   threw, s**ou**p, thr**ou**gh, sh**oe**, tw**o**,
   fr**ui**t, man**eu**ver, li**eu**tenant, b**eau**ty,
   v**ie**w, vac**uu**m, rh**eu**matism, br**ou**gham
v **v**ery, ha**v**e, o**f**, **St**ephen
w **w**ill, **q**uick
y **y**es, opin**i**on
z **z**ero, **x**ylophone, ha**s**, bu**zz**, **s**cissors,
   a**s**thma, ra**s**pberry
zh mea**s**ure, gara**g**e, divi**s**ion
ə **a**lone, compl**e**te, mom**e**nt, **au**thority,
   barg**ai**n, Apr**i**l, cauti**ou**s, circ**u**s, tort**oi**se,
   cupb**oa**rd, parli**a**ment, ging**ha**m

*Not all English spellings of these sounds are included in this list.

Full pronunciation key

a	hat, cap	**o**	hot, rock
ā	age, face	**ō**	open, go
ä	father, far	**ô**	order, all
		oi	oil, voice
		ou	house, out
b	bad, rob		
ch	child, much	**p**	paper, cup
d	did, red	**r**	run, try
		s	say, yes
e	let, best	**sh**	she, rush
ē	equal, be	**t**	tell, it
ėr	term, learn	**th**	thin, both
		ᴛʜ	then, smooth
f	fat, if		
g	go, bag	**u**	cup, butter
h	he, how	**ủ**	full, put
		ü	rule, move
i	it, pin		
ī	ice, five	**v**	very, save
		w	will, woman
j	jam, enjoy	**y**	young, yet
k	kind, seek	**z**	zero, breeze
l	land, coal	**zh**	measure, seizure
m	me, am		
n	no, in		
ng	long, bring		

ə represents:
a in about
e in taken
i in pencil
o in lemon
u in circus

The contents of the glossary entries in this book have been adapted from the *Thorndike Barnhart Advanced Dictionary*, copyright © 1974 by Scott, Foresman and Company.

ac com plice (ə kom′plis), *n.* person who knowingly aids another in committing a crime or other wrong act: *Without an accomplice to open the door the thief could not have got into the house so easily.*

ac count ant (ə koun′tənt), *n.* person whose profession is examining or interpreting business accounts and financial records.

ac cused (ə kyüzd′), *n.* **the accused,** the person or persons formally charged with an offense or a crime in a court of law.

ac quit tal (ə kwit′l), *n.* an acquitting; discharge; release.

a dapt (ə dapt′), *v.t.* **1** make fit or suitable; adjust: *adapt one's way of working to the needs of the job.* **2** modify or alter so as to make fit or suitable for a different use or a particular place or purpose: *The story was adapted for the movies from a novel.* [< Latin *adaptare* < *ad-* to + *aptus* fitted, suitable]

a dopt (ə dopt′), *v.t.* **1** take or use as one's own choice: *adopt an idea, adopt a new custom.* **2** take (a child of other parents), as approved by law, and bring up as one's own child. [< Latin *adoptare* < *ad-* to + *optare* choose]

af fect (ə fekt′), *v.t.* have an effect on; act on; influence or change: *Nothing you say will affect my decision. The disease affected her eyesight.* [< Latin *affectum* done to, acted on < *ad-* to + *facere* do]

al ba tross (al′bə trôs, al′bə tros), *n., pl.* **-tross es** or **-tross.** any of various web-footed sea birds related to the petrel, noted as the largest sea birds and for their ability to fly long distances. [ultimately < Arabic *alghaṭṭās,* a sea eagle]

albatross
30 in. long, wingspread up to 11½ ft.

al le giance (ə lē′jəns), *n.* **1** the loyalty owed by a citizen to his country; obligation of a subject to his ruler or government. **2** faithfulness to a person, cause, etc.; loyalty; fidelity. [Middle English *alegeaunce* < Old French *ligeance* < *lige* liege]

al lude (ə lüd′), *v.i.,* **-lud ed, -lud ing.** refer indirectly *(to);* mention slightly in passing: *I didn't tell him of your decision; I didn't even allude to it.*

ap a thy (ap′ə thē), *n., pl.* **-thies. 1** lack of interest in or desire for activity. **2** lack of feeling. [< Greek *apatheia* < *a-* without + *pathos* feeling]

as ton ish (ə ston′ish), *v.t.* surprise greatly; amaze; astound.

a the ist (ā′thē ist), *n.* person who does not believe in the existence of God.

at tor ney (ə tėr′nē), *n., pl.* **-neys. 1** person who has power to act for another in business or legal matters. **2** lawyer.

au to bi og ra phy (ô′tə bī og′rə fē, ô′tə bē og′rə fē), *n., pl.* **-phies.** account of a person's life written by himself.

au to mat ic (ô′tə mat′ik), *adj.* **1** (of machinery, etc.) moving or acting by itself; regulating itself: *an automatic pump, an automatic elevator.* **2** done normally without thought or attention; not voluntary: *Breathing and swallowing are usually automatic.* [< Greek *automatos* self-acting] —**au′to mat′i cal ly,** *adv.*

bi cy cle (bī′sik/əl, bī′sə kəl), *n., v.,* **-cled, -cling.** —*n.* a lightweight vehicle consisting of a metal frame with two wheels, one behind the other, a handlebar for steering, a seat for the rider, and pedals propelled by pressure of the feet. —*v.i.* ride or travel on a bicycle. [< *bi-* two + Greek *kyklos* circle, wheel] —**bi′cy cler,** *n.*

bi lin gual (bī ling′gwəl), *adj.* **1** able to speak another language as well or almost as well as one's own. **2** containing or written in two languages: *a bilingual dictionary.*

bi noc u lars (bə nok′yə lərz, bī nok′yə lərz), *n.pl.* a double telescope joined as a unit for use with both eyes simultaneously, such as field glasses.

bi og ra phy (bī og′rə fē, bē og′rə fē), *n., pl.* **-phies.** an account of a person's life.

bi ol o gy (bī ol′ə jē), *n.* the scientific study of plant and animal life, including its origin, structure, activities, and distribution. Botany, zoology, and ecology are branches of biology.

browse (brouz), *v.,* **browsed, brows ing.** —*v.i.* **1** read here and there in a book. **2** pass the time looking at books in a library, bookstore, etc. —**brows′er,** *n.*

can ta loupe or **can ta loup** (kan′tl ōp), *n.* kind of muskmelon with a hard, rough rind and sweet, juicy, orange flesh. [< French *cantaloup* < Italian *Cantalupo* papal estate near Rome where first cultivated]

ca reer (kə rir′), *n.* **1** a general course of action or progress through life: *It is interesting to read of the careers of great men and women.* **2** occupation; profession: *She planned to make law her career.*

cau li flow er (kô′lə flou′ər, kol′ē flou′ər), *n.* **1** species of cole, related to the cabbage, having a solid, white head with a few leaves around it. **2** its head, which is eaten as a vegetable. [< Latin *caulis* cabbage + *florem* flower]

cauliflower ear, INFORMAL. ear that has been misshapen by injuries received in boxing, etc.

cease (sēs), *v.,* **ceased, ceas ing.** —*v.i.* come to an end; stop: *The storm ceased suddenly.* —*v.t.* put an end or stop to: *Cease trying to do more than you can.*

cen ti grade (sen′tə grād), *adj.* of, based on, or according to a scale for measuring temperature on which 0 degrees marks the freezing point of water and 100 degrees marks the boiling point. [< French < Latin *centum* hundred + *gradus* degree]

chap e ron or **chap e rone** (shap′ə rōn′), *n., v.,* **-roned, -ron ing.** —*n.* an older person who is present at a party or other social activity of young people. —*v.t.* act as a chaperon to. [< Old French *chaperon* hood, protector]

char i ty (char′ə tē), *n., pl.* **-ties.** **1** a generous giving to the poor, or to organizations which look after the sick, the poor, and the helpless. **2** fund, institution, or organization for helping the sick, the poor, and the helpless. [< Old French *charite* < Latin *caritatem* affection < *carus* dear]

chim ney (chim′nē), *n., pl.* **-neys.** **1** an upright structure of brick or stone, connected with a fireplace, furnace, etc., to make a draft and carry away smoke. **2** a glass tube placed around the flame of a lamp.

choose (chüz), *v.,* **chose, cho sen, choos ing.** —*v.t.* **1** pick out; select from a number: *She chose a book from the library.* **2** prefer and decide; think fit: *I did not choose to go.*

chose (chōz), *v.* pt. of **choose.** *She chose the red dress to wear.*

chron ic (kron′ik), *adj.* **1** lasting a long time: *Rheumatism is often a chronic disease.* **2** suffering long from an illness: *a chronic invalid.* **3** never stopping; constant; habitual: *a chronic liar.* [< Greek *chronos* time]

chro nom e ter (krə nom′ə tər), *n.* clock or watch that keeps very accurate time. A ship's chronometer is used in determining longitude.

cloak (klōk), *n.* a loose outer garment with or without sleeves; mantle. —*v.t.* cover up; conceal; hide. [< Old French *cloque* < Late Latin *clocca*, originally, bell. Doublet of CLOCHE, CLOCK.]

clout (klout), *v.t.* INFORMAL. hit with the hand; rap; knock; cuff. —*n.* **1** INFORMAL. a hit with the hand; a rap; a knock; a cuff. **2** INFORMAL. political force, power, or influence.

col lect i ble (kə lek′tə bəl), *adj.* able to be collected. Also, **collectable.**

com pas sion (kəm pash′ən), *n.* feeling for another's sorrow or hardship that leads to help; sympathy; pity. [< Latin *compassionem* < *compati* suffer with < *com-* with + *pati* suffer]

com pro mise (kom′prə mīz), *v.,* **-mised, -mis ing,** *n.* —*v.t.* settle (a dispute) by agreeing that each will give up a part of what he demands. —*n.* **1** settlement of a dispute by a partial yielding on both sides. **2** result of such a settlement. [< Latin *compromittere* promise together < *com-* together + *promittere* promise]

com pul sor y (kəm pul′sər ē), *adj.* **1** compelled; required: *Attendance at school is compulsory for children.* **2** compelling; using force.

con fi dent (kon′fə dənt), *adj.* **1** firmly believing; certain; sure. **2** sure of oneself and one's abilities. **3** too bold; too sure. —**con′fi dent ly,** *adv.*

con science (kon′shəns), *n.* sense of right and wrong; ideas and feelings within a person that warn him of what is wrong. —**con′science less,** *adj.*

con sci en tious (kon′shē en′shəs), *adj.* **1** careful to do what one knows is right; controlled by conscience. **2** done with care to make it right; painstaking: *conscientious work.* —**con′sci en′tious ly,** *adv.*

con sid er a ble (kən sid′ər ə bəl), *adj.* **1** worth thinking about; important: *a considerable responsibility.* **2** not a little; much: *a considerable sum of money.*

cor du roy (kôr′də roi′, kôr′də roi′), *n.* **1** a thick, cotton cloth with close, velvetlike ridges. **2** **corduroys,** *pl.* corduroy trousers. —*adj.* made of corduroy. [< *cord,* noun + obsolete *duroy,* a type of woolen cloth]

coun se lor or **coun sel lor** (koun′sə lər), *n.* **1** person who gives advice; adviser. **2** lawyer. **3** instructor or leader at a camp.

cow ard (kou′ərd), *n.* person who lacks courage or is easily made afraid; person who runs from danger, trouble, etc. —*adj.* lacking courage; cowardly. [< Old French *coart* < *coe* tail < Latin *coda, cauda;* with reference to an animal with its tail between its legs]

crack pot (krak′pot′), *n.* SLANG. a very eccentric person. —*adj.* eccentric or impractical: *crackpot ideas.*

cri ter i on (krī tir′ē ən), *n., pl.* **-ter i a** or **-ter i ons.** rule or standard for making a judgment; test: *Wealth is only one criterion of success.* [< Greek *kritērion* < *krinein* decide, judge]

dec ade (dek′ād), *n.* **1** period of ten years. **2** group, set, or series of ten. [< Greek *deka* ten]

Dec a logue or **Dec a log** (dek′ə lôg, dek′ə log), *n.* **1** (in the Bible) the Ten Commandments. **2 decalogue** or **dec-alog,** any set of ten commandments or rules. [< Greek *dekalogos* < *deka* ten + *logos* word]

de lib er ate (*adj.* di lib′ər it; *v.* di lib′ə rāt′), *adj., v.,* **-at ed, -at ing.** —*adj.* **1** carefully thought out beforehand; made or done on purpose; intended: *a deliberate lie.* **2** slow and careful in deciding what to do; thoughtful. —*v.t.* think over carefully; consider. [< Latin *deliberatum* carefully weighed < *de-* + *librare* weigh] —**de lib′er ate ly,** *adv.*

de moc ra cy (di mok′rə sē), *n., pl.* **-cies.** **1** government that is run by the people who live under it. In a democracy the people rule either directly through meetings that all may attend, such as the town meetings in New England, or indirectly through the election of certain representatives. **2** country, state, or community having such a government. [< Greek *dēmokratia* < *dēmos* people + *kratos* rule]

de pressed (di prest′), *adj.* **1** gloomy; low-spirited; sad. **2** pressed down; lowered.

de tec tive (di tek′tiv), *n.* member of a police force or other person whose work is finding information by investigation, to discover who committed a crime, etc. —*adj.* having to do with detectives and their work: *a detective story.*

die sel or **Die sel** (dē′zl, dē′sl), *n.* **1** diesel engine. **2** a truck, locomotive, train, etc., with a diesel engine. —*adj.* **1** equipped with or run by a diesel engine: *a diesel tractor.* **2** of or for a diesel engine: *diesel fuel.* [< Rudolf *Diesel,* 1858-1913, German engineer who invented the diesel engine]

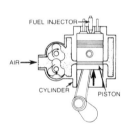

FUEL INJECTOR
AIR
CYLINDER
PISTON

diesel engine—Air entering the cylinder is compressed by the piston and becomes very hot. A spray of oil sent into the air burns, causing a forceful expansion of the gas, which forces the piston down.

dis cern (də zèrn′, də sèrn′), *v.t.* see clearly; perceive the difference between (two or more things); distinguish or recognize: *We discerned the island through the mist.*

dis cern i ble (də zèr′nə bəl, də sèr′nə bəl), *adj.* capable of being discerned. —**dis cern′i bly,** *adv.*

disk (disk), *n.* **1** a round, flat, thin object shaped like a coin. **2** a phonograph record. Also, **disc.** [< Latin *discus* discus < Greek *diskos.* Doublet of DAIS, DESK, DISCUS, and DISH.]

doc u men tar y (dok′yə men′tər ē), *adj., n., pl.* **-tar ies.** —*adj.* presenting or recording factual information in an artistic fashion: *a documentary film.* —*n.* a documentary motion picture, book, or radio or television program.

dom i nate (dom′ə nāt), *v.,* **-nat ed, -nat ing.** —*v.t.* **1** control or rule by strength or power. **2** rise high above; tower over: *The mountain dominates the city and its harbor.* [< Latin *dominatum* ruled < *dominum* lord, master]

a hat | i it | oi oil | ch child
ā age | ī ice | ou out | ng long
ä far | o hot | u cup | sh she
e let | ō open | ů put | th thin
ē equal | ô order | ü rule | ᴛʜ then
ėr term | | | zh measure

ə = { a in about / e in taken / i in pencil / o in lemon / u in circus }

drench (drench), *v.t.* wet thoroughly; soak: *A heavy rain drenched the campers.* [Old English *drencan* < *drincan* to drink]

drown (droun), *v.i.* die under water or other liquid because of lack of air to breathe. —*v.t.* **1** kill by keeping under water or other liquid. **2** cover with water; flood. **3** be stronger or louder than; keep from being heard: *The boat's whistle drowned out the directions she was trying to give us.*

dum found (dum′found′), *v.t.* amaze and make unable to speak; bewilder; confuse. Also, **dumbfound.**

ef fect (ə fekt′), *n.* **1** whatever is produced by a cause; something made to happen by a person or thing; result. **2** influence: *The medicine had an immediate effect.* —*v.t.* make happen; bring about.

e lude (i lüd′), *v.t.,* **e lud ed, e lud ing.** avoid or escape by cleverness, quickness, etc.; slip away from; evade: *The sly fox eluded the dogs.* [< Latin *eludere* < *ex-* out + *ludere* to play]

e merge (i mėrj′), *v.i.,* **e merged, e merg ing.** **1** come into view; come out; come up: *The sun emerged from behind a cloud.* **2** become known: *New facts emerged as a result of a second investigation.* [< Latin *emergere* < *ex-* out + *mergere* to dip]

em pa thy (em′pə thē), *n.* (in psychology) the quality or process of entering fully, through imagination, into another's feelings or motives. [< Greek *empatheia* < *en-* in + *pathos* feeling]

ep i dem ic (ep′ə dem′ik), *n.* the rapid spread of a disease so that many people have it at the same time: *a flu epidemic.* —*adj.* affecting many people at the same time; widespread: *an epidemic disease.* [< Greek *épidemia* a stay, visit, prevalence (of a disease) < *epi-* among + *démos* people]

e vap o rate (i vap′ə rāt′), *v.,* **-rat ed, -rat ing.** —*v.i.* change from a liquid into a vapor: *Boiling water evaporates rapidly.* —*v.t.* cause to change into a vapor: *Heat evaporates water.* [< Latin *evaporatum* evaporated < *ex-* out + *vapor* vapor]

ev i dence (ev′ə dəns), *n.* **1** anything that shows what is true and what is not; facts; proof: *The evidence showed that he had not been near the place.* **2** facts established and accepted in a court of law. Before deciding a case, the judge or jury hears all the evidence given by both sides.

ex per i ment (*v.* ek sper′ə ment; *n.* ek sper′ə mənt), *v.i.* try something in order to find out about it; make trials or tests: *That painter is experimenting with different paints to get the color he wants.* —*n.* trial or test to find out or discover something unknown, to verify a hypothesis, or to illustrate some known truth. —**ex per′i ment er,** *n.*

fla men co (flə meng′kō), *n., pl.* **-cos.** style of Spanish Gypsy dance performed with castanets to fast, fiery, vigorous rhythms. [< Spanish, literally, Flemish (applied to the Gypsies' dance celebrating their departure from Germany, later confused with Flanders)]

for mer ly (fôr′mər lē), *adv.* at an earlier time; some time ago; previously.

frus trate (frus′trāt), *v.t.,* **-trat ed, -trat ing. 1** make useless or worthless; bring to nothing; foil; defeat. **2** prevent from accomplishing; thwart; oppose: *frustrated in one's ambition.* [< Latin *frustratum* disappointed < *frustra* in vain]

fun gus (fung′gəs), *n., pl.* **fun gi** or **fun gus es,** *adj.* —*n.* any of a subdivision of plants without flowers, leaves, or chlorophyll that get their nourishment from dead or living organic matter and reproduce by spores and division. Mushrooms, yeasts, toadstools, molds, and mildews are fungi. —*adj.* fungous. [< Latin]

fungus
fungi growing on a tree

ge ol o gy (jē ol′ə jē), *n., pl.* **-gies. 1** science that deals with the earth's crust, the layers of which it is composed, and their history. **2** features of the earth's crust in a region; rocks, rock formation, etc., of a particular area: *the geology of North America.*

ge om e try (jē om′ə trē), *n., pl.* **-tries.** branch of mathematics which studies the relationship of points, lines, angles, and surfaces of figures in space; the mathematics of space. Geometry includes the definition, comparison, and measurement of squares, triangles, circles, cubes, cones, and other plane and solid figures. [< Greek *geōmetria* < *gē* earth + *-metria* measuring]

gher kin (gėr′kən), *n.* **1** a small, prickly cucumber often used for pickles. **2** the plant it grows on. **3** any young, green cucumber used for pickles. [< Dutch *gurken,* plural of *gurk* < Slavic]

gon er (gô′nər, gon′ər), *n.* INFORMAL. person or thing that is dead, ruined, or past help.

gran ite (gran′it), *n.* a hard, igneous rock made of grains of other rocks, chiefly quartz and feldspar, much used for buildings and monuments. [< Italian *granito* grained < *grano* grain < Latin *granum*]

grant (grant), *v.t.* **1** give what is asked; allow: *grant a request, grant permission.* **2 take for granted,** accept as probable: *We took for granted that the sailor could swim.* [< Old French *granter, creanter* to promise, authorize, ultimately < Latin *credere* to trust]

grouch y (grou′chē), *adj.,* **grouch i er, grouch i est.** INFORMAL. tending to grumble or complain; surly; ill-tempered. —**grouch′i ness,** *n.*

hy giene (hī′jēn′), *n.* science that deals with the maintenance of health; system of principles or rules for preserving or promoting health. [< French *hygiène,* ultimately < Greek *hygies* healthy]

im par tial (im pär′shəl), *adj.* showing no more favor to one side than to the other; fair; just. —**im par′tial ly,** *adv.*

im ply (im plī′), *v.t.,* **-plied, -ply ing.** mean without saying so; express indirectly; suggest: *Her smile implied that she had forgiven us.*

im pro vise (im′prə vīz), *v.,* **-vised, -vis ing.** —*v.t.* make up (music, poetry, etc.) on the spur of the moment; sing, recite, speak, etc., without preparation. [< Latin *in-* not + *pro-* beforehand + *videre* see] —**im′pro vis′er,** *n.*

in fer (in fėr′), *v.,* **-ferred, -fer ring.** —*v.t.* find out by a process of reasoning from something known or assumed; conclude: *People inferred that so able a governor would make a good President.*

in ter est ing (in′tər ə sting, in′tə res′ting), *adj.* arousing interest; holding one's attention. —**in′ter est ing ly,** *adv.*

in ter view (in′tər vyü), *n.* **1** a meeting, generally of persons face to face, to talk over something special. **2** a meeting between a reporter, writer, radio or television commentator, etc., and a person from whom information is sought for publication or broadcast. —*v.t.* have an interview with; meet and talk with, especially to obtain information. —**in′ter view′er,** *n.*

is sue (ish′ü), *v.,* **-sued, -su ing.** —*v.t.* send out; put forth: *The government issues money and stamps.* —*v.i.* come out; go out: *Smoke issues from the chimney.*

i tem ize (ī′tə mīz), *v.t.,* **-ized, -iz ing.** give each item of; list by items: *itemize a bill.*

i tin e rar y (ī tin′ə rer′ē, i tin′ə rer′ē), *n., pl.* **-rar ies. 1** route of travel; plan of travel. **2** record of travel. **3** guidebook for travelers.

kid (kid), *v.,* **kid ded, kid ding.** SLANG. —*v.t.* **1** tease playfully. **2** deceive; fool. —*v.i.* talk jokingly; banter. —**kid′der,** *n.*

launch (lônch, länch), *v.t.* **1** cause to slide into the water; set afloat: *A new ship is launched from the supports on which it was built.* **2** push out or put forth into the air: *launch a plane from an aircraft carrier.* **3** set going; start: *Our friends launched us in business by lending us money.*

lib e rate (lib′ə rāt′), *v.t.,* **-rat ed, -rat ing.** set free; free or release from slavery, prison, confinement, etc. [< Latin *liberatum* freed < *liber* free] —**lib′e ra′tor,** *n.*

liq ue fy (lik′wə fī), *v.t., v.i.,* **-fied, -fy ing.** change into a liquid; make or become liquid: *Liquefied air is extremely cold.*

lit e ra ture (lit′ər ə chur, lit′ər ə chər), *n.* **1** the body of writings of a period, language, or country: *English literature.* **2** the study of literature: *I shall take literature and mathematics this spring.*

loose (lüs), *adj.,* **loos er, loos est. 1** not fastened or attached; untied: *a loose thread.* **2** not tight; slack: *loose clothing, loose reins.* [< Scandinavian (Old Icelandic) *lauss*] —**loose′ly,** *adv.* —**loose′ness,** *n.*

lose (lüz), *v.,* **lost, los ing.** —*v.t.* **1** not have any longer; have taken away from one by accident, carelessness, parting, death, etc.: *lose a finger, lose a friend, lose one's life.* **2** fail to win: *lose the prize, lose a bet, lose a game.* —*v.i.* be defeated: *Our team lost.* —**los′er,** *n.*

man u fac ture (man/yə fak/chər), *v.*, **-tured, -tur ing**, *n.*
—*v.t.* make by hand or by machine; produce by human labor, especially in large quantities: *manufacture steel, manufacture furniture.* —*n.* act or process of manufacturing. [< Middle French < Medieval Latin *manufactura* < Latin *manu facere* make by hand]

mer chan dise (mér/chən dīz), *n.*, *v.*, **-dised, -dis ing**. —*n.* goods for sale; articles bought and sold; wares. —*v.t.*, *v.i.* **1** buy and sell; trade. **2** further the sales of (goods and services) by advertising and other methods. —**mer/chan dis/er**, *n.*

mis cel la ne ous (mis/ə lā/nē əs), *adj.* **1** not all of one kind or nature; of mixed composition or character: *miscellaneous expenses.* **2** dealing with various subjects. [< Latin *miscellaneus* < *miscellus* mixed < *miscere* to mix] —**mis/cel la/ne ous ly**, *adv.*

mis chief (mis/chif), *n.* **1** conduct that causes harm or trouble, often unintentionally. **2** harm or injury, usually done by some person.

mod ern (mod/ərn), *adj.* **1** of present or recent time; of or in the current age or period: *Color television is a modern invention.* **2** up-to-date; not old-fashioned.

mol e cule (mol/ə kyül), *n.* **1** the smallest particle into which an element or compound can be divided without changing its chemical and physical properties. A molecule of an element consists of one or more like atoms. A molecule of a compound consists of two or more different atoms. **2** a very small particle.

mo nop o ly (mə nop/ə lē), *n.*, *pl.* **-lies. 1** the exclusive control of a commodity or service: *The only milk company in town has a monopoly on milk delivery.* **2** the exclusive possession or control of something: *a monopoly of a person's time.* [< Greek *monopolion* < *mono-* + *pōlein* to sell]

mo not o nous (mə not/n əs), *adj.* **1** continuing in the same tone or pitch: *a monotonous voice.* **2** not varying; without change. **3** wearying because of its sameness; tedious: *monotonous work.* —**mo not/o nous ly**, *adv.*

mous tache (mus/tash, mə stash/), *n.* mustache.

mov a ble (mü/və bəl), *adj.* that can be moved; not fixed in one place or position: *Our fingers are movable.* Also, **moveable.**

mus tache (mus/tash, mə stash/), *n.* **1** hair growing on a man's upper lip. **2** hairs or bristles growing near the mouth of an animal. Also, **moustache.** [< French *moustache* < Italian *mostacchio* < Medieval Latin *mustacia* < Greek *mystax* upper lip, mustache]

neb u la (neb/yə lə), *n.*, *pl.* **-lae** (-lē/), **-las.** a cloudlike cluster of stars or a hazy mass of dust particles and gases which occurs in interstellar space and which may be either dark or illuminated by surrounding stars. [< Latin, mist, cloud]

neu tron (nü/tron, nyü/tron), *n.* an elementary particle with a neutral charge that occurs in the nucleus of every atom except hydrogen and has about the same mass as a proton. Neutrons are used to bombard the nuclei of various elements to produce fission and other nuclear reactions.

no tice a ble (nō/ti sə bəl), *adj.* **1** easily seen or noticed: *The class has made noticeable improvement.* **2** worth noticing. —**no/tice a bly**, *adv.*

a hat	i it	oi oil	ch child		a in about
ā age	ī ice	ou out	ng long		e in taken
ä far	o hot	u cup	sh she	ə =	i in pencil
e let	ō open	u̇ put	th thin		o in lemon
ē equal	ô order	ü rule	ŦH then		u in circus
ėr term			zh measure		

nu cle us (nü/klē əs, nyü/klē əs), *n.*, *pl.* **-cle i** or **-cle us es. 1** a central part or thing around which other parts or things are collected. **2** the central part of an atom, consisting of a proton or protons, neutrons, and other particles. **3** (in biology) a mass of specialized protoplasm found in most plant and animal cells without which the cell cannot grow and divide. [< Latin, kernel < *nux, nucis* nut]

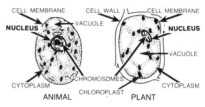

animal cell and plant cell, greatly magnified

oc ta gon (ok/tə gon, ok/tə gən), *n.* a plane figure having eight angles and eight sides. [< Greek *oktagōnos* < *okta* eight + *gōnia* angle]

oc tave (ok/tiv, ok/tāv), *n.* **1** interval between a musical tone and another tone having twice or half as many vibrations. From middle C to the C above it is an octave. **2** group of eight. [< Latin *octo* eight]

out ra geous (out rā/jəs), *adj.* very offensive or insulting; shocking. —**out ra/geous ly**, *adv.*

out wit (out wit/), *v.t.*, **-wit ted, -wit ting.** get the better of by being more intelligent; be too clever for.

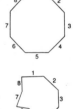

octagon
top, regular
bottom, irregular

pan to mime (pan/tə mīm), *n.*, *v.*, **-mimed, -mim ing.** —*n.* **1** a play without words, in which the actors express themselves by gestures. **2** gestures without words. **3** mime or mimic, especially in the ancient Roman theater. —*v.t.* express by gestures. [< Greek *pantomimos* < *pantos* all + *mimos* mimic]

par tic u lar ly (pər tik/yə lər lē), *adv.* **1** in a high degree; especially. **2** in a particular manner; in all its parts; in detail; minutely.

pa tron ize (pā/trə nīz, pat/rə nīz), *v.t.*, **-ized, -iz ing. 1** be a regular customer of; give regular business to: *We patronize our neighborhood stores.* **2** treat in a haughty, condescending way.

pen ta gon (pen′tə gon), *n.* a plane figure having five sides and five angles. [< Greek *pentagōnon* < *penta-* + *gōnia* angle]

per jur y (pėr′jər ē), *n., pl.* **-jur ies.** act or crime of willfully giving false testimony or withholding evidence while under oath; a swearing falsely.

phe nom e non (fə nom′ə non), *n., pl.* **-na. 1** fact, event, or circumstance that can be observed: *Lightning is an electrical phenomenon.* **2** any exceptional fact or occurrence: *historical phenomena.* [< Greek *phainomenon* < *phainesthai* appear]

pho to syn the sis (fō′tō sin′thə sis), *n.* **1** process by which plant cells make carbohydrates by combining carbon dioxide and water in the presence of chlorophyll and light, and release oxygen as a by-product. **2** process by which chemical compounds are synthesized by means of light or other forms of radiant energy.

poke (pōk), *n.* DIALECT. bag; sack.

pos ses sive (pə zes′iv), *adj.* **1** of possession. **2** showing possession. *My, your, his,* and *our* are in the possessive case because they indicate who possesses or owns. —*n.* **1** the possessive case. **2** word in this case. In "the boy's books," *boy's* is a possessive.

prac tice (prak′tis), *n., v.,* **-ticed, -tic ing.** —*n.* action done many times over for the purpose, or with the result, of acquiring skill or proficiency: *Practice makes perfect.* —*v.t.* do (some act) again and again for the purpose, or with the result, of acquiring skill or proficiency: *practice playing the piano.*

pre ced ing (prē sē′ding), *adj.* going or coming before; previous.

pre miere (pri mir′, prə myer′), *n., v.,* **-miered, -mier ing.** —*n.* a first public performance: *the premiere of a new play.* —*v.i.* have the first public performance or showing: *The movie is premiering today.* [< French *première*]

pro ceed (prə sēd′), *v.i.* **1** go on after a stop or interruption; move forward; continue: *Please proceed with your story.* **2** be carried on; take place: *The trial may proceed.* [< Latin *procedere* < *pro-* forward + *cedere* to move]

pro gres sive (prə gres′iv), *adj.* **1** making progress; advancing to something better; improving: *a progressive nation.* **2** favoring progress; wanting improvement or reform. —*n.* person who favors improvement and reform in government, religion, or business, etc.

pro noun (prō′noun), *n.* word used instead of a noun to designate an object or person without naming, when the object or person referred to is known from the context or has already been mentioned. EXAMPLES: I, we, you, he, it, they, who, whose, which, this, mine, whatever. [< Latin *pronomen* < *pro-* in place of + *nomen* name, noun]

prop a gan da (prop′ə gan′də), *n.* **1** systematic effort to spread opinions or beliefs; any plan or method for spreading opinions or beliefs: *Clever propaganda misled the enemy into believing it could not win the war.* **2** opinions or beliefs thus spread.

pros e cu tion (pros′ə kyü′shən), *n.* side that starts action against another in a court of law. The prosecution makes certain charges against the defense.

pentagon
top, regular;
bottom, irregular

prowl (proul), *v.i.* go about slowly and secretly hunting for something to eat or steal: *Many wild animals prowl at night.* —**prowl′er,** *n.*

quad ran gle (kwod′rang′gəl), *n.* **1** a four-sided space or court wholly or nearly surrounded by buildings: *a college quadrangle.* **2** buildings around a quadrangle. **3** quadrilateral. [< Latin *quadr-* four + *angulus* angle]

qual i ty (kwol′ə tē), *n., pl.* **-ties. 1** something special about an object that makes it what it is; essential attribute; characteristic: *Sweetness is a quality of sugar.* **2** grade of excellence; degree of worth: *food of poor quality. That is the finest quality of cloth.* **3** fineness; merit; excellence. [< Latin *qualitatem* < *qualis* of what sort]

quit (kwit), *v.,* **quit** or **quit ted, quit ting,** —*v.t.* **1** stop, cease, or discontinue: *quit work at five.* **2** give up; let go: *quit a job.* [< Old French *quiter* < *quite* free, clear < Latin *quietus* at rest.]

quite (kwīt), *adv.* **1** completely; wholly; entirely: *a hat quite out of fashion.* **2** INFORMAL. to a considerable extent or degree: *I hiked quite a distance. He is quite worried about his grandparents' health.* A number of convenient phrases with *quite* are good informal usage: *quite a few* people, *quite a long* time, etc.

ra di o ac tive (rā′dē ō ak′tiv), *adj.* of, having, or caused by radioactivity. Radium, uranium, and thorium are radioactive metallic elements.

rec og nize (rek′əg nīz), *v.t.,* **-nized, -niz ing. 1** be aware of (someone or something) as already known; know again: *recognize an old friend.* **2** take notice of: *The delegate waited till the chairman recognized him.*

re duc i ble (ri dü′sə bəl, ri dyü′sə bəl), *adj.* able to be reduced: $4/8$ is reducible to $1/2$.

re gal (rē′gəl), *adj.* **1** belonging to a king; royal. **2** fit for a king; kinglike; stately; splendid; magnificent. [< Latin *regalis* < *regem* king. Doublet of ROYAL, REAL, RIAL.] —**re′gal ly,** *adv.*

re lax (ri laks′), *v.t., v.i.* **1** make or become less stiff or firm; loosen up: *Relax your muscles to rest them.* **2** make or become less strict or severe; lessen in force: *Discipline was relaxed on the last day of school.* [< Latin *relaxare* < *re-* back + *laxus* loose.]

re spon si ble (ri spon′sə bəl), *adj.* obliged or expected to account *(for)*; accountable; answerable: *Each pupil is responsible for the care of the books given him.* —**re spon′si bly,** *adv.*

re vise (ri vīz′), *v.,* **-vised, -vis ing.** —*v.t.* read carefully in order to correct; look over and change; examine and improve: *revise a manuscript.* [< Latin *revisere* see again < *re-* again + *videre* to see] —**re vis′er, re vi′sor,** *n.*

schuss (shùs), in skiing: —*n.* **1** a fast run down a straight course. **2** the course itself. —*v.i.* to make a run at top speed over a straight course. [< German *Schuss,* literally, shot]

scoun drel (skoun′drəl), *n.* person without honor or good principles; villain; rascal.

serv ice (sér′vis), *n., v.,* **-iced, -ic ing.** —*n.* **1** helpful act or acts; aid; conduct that is useful to others: *perform a service for one's country.* **2** arrangements for supplying something useful or necessary: *The train service was good.* **3** manner of serving food. —*v.t.* make fit for service; keep fit for service. [< Old French < Latin *servitium* < *servus* slave]

slouch (slouch), *v.i.* stand, sit, walk, or move in an awkward, drooping manner: *The weary man slouched along.* —*n.* a bending forward of head and shoulders; awkward, drooping way of standing, sitting, or walking. —**slouch′er,** *n.*

sov er eign (sov′rən), *n.* supreme ruler; king or queen; monarch. —*adj.* having the rank or power of a sovereign. [< Old French *soverain,* ultimately < Latin *super* over]

spe cial ize (spesh′ə līz), *v.,* **-ized, -iz ing.** —*v.i.* pursue some special branch of study, work, etc.: *Many students specialize in engineering.* —**spe′cial i za′tion,** *n.*

stat ic (stat′ik), *adj.* **1** in a fixed or stable condition; not in a state of progress or change; at rest; standing still: *Civilization does not remain static, but changes constantly.* **2** having to do with stationary electrical charges. Static electricity can be produced by rubbing a glass rod with a silk cloth. —*n.* electrical disturbances in the air, caused by electrical storms, etc. [< Greek *statikos* causing to stand, ultimately < *histanai* cause to stand]

strength (strengkth, strength), *n.* **1** quality of being strong; power; force: *Samson was a man of great strength.* **2** power to resist force: *the strength of a beam.* **3 on the strength of,** relying or depending on; with the support or help of.

suf frage (suf′rij), *n.* the right to vote; franchise: *The United States granted suffrage to women in 1920.* [< Latin *suffragium* supporting vote]

sum ma rize (sum′ə rīz′), *v.t., v.i.,* **-rized, -riz ing.** make a summary of; give only the main points of; express briefly. —**sum′ma ri za′tion,** *n.*

sum mar y (sum′ər ē), *n., pl.* **-mar ies.** —*n.* a brief statement giving the main points: *The history book had a summary at the end of each chapter.* [< Latin *summarium* < *summa* sum]

sur round ings (sə roun′dingz), *n.pl.* surrounding things, conditions, etc.; environment.

sym bol ize (sim′bə līz), *v.,* **-ized, -iz ing.** —*v.t.* **1** be a symbol of; stand for; represent: *A dove symbolizes peace.* **2** represent by a symbol or symbols.

sym pa thet ic (sim′pə thet′ik), *adj.* **1** having or showing kind feelings toward others; sympathizing. **2** approving; agreeing. —**sym′pa thet′i cal ly,** *adv.*

tax i (tak′sē), *v.,* **tax ied, tax i ing** or **tax y ing.** —*v.i.* **1** ride in a taxicab. **2** (of an aircraft) move across the ground or water under its own power before take-off or after landing. —*v.t.* **1** cause (an aircraft) to taxi. **2** take in a taxicab.

tes ti fy (tes′tə fī), *v.,* **-fied, -fy ing.** —*v.i.* **1** give evidence; bear witness. **2** give evidence under oath in a court of law: *The witness was unwilling to testify.* —*v.t.* declare under oath in a court of law: *The witness testified that the speeding car had crashed into the truck.* [< Latin *testificari* < *testis* witness + *facere* to make]

the a ter (thē′ə tər), *n.* **1** place where plays are acted or motion pictures are shown. **2** the writing, performance, or production of plays; drama. Also, **theatre.** [< Greek *theatron* < *theasthai* to view]

the a tre (thē′ə tər), *n.* theater.

the ol o gy (thē ol′ə jē), *n., pl.* **-gies. 1** doctrines concerning God and His relations to man and the universe. **2** study of religion and religious beliefs. [< Greek *theologia* < *theos* god + *-logia* -logy]

ther mo stat (thér′mə stat), *n.* an automatic device for regulating temperature. [< *thermo-* + Greek *-statēs* that stands]

trail (trāl), *n.* path across a wild or unsettled region: *a mountain trail.*

tri al (trī′əl), *n.* the examining and deciding of a civil or criminal case in a court of law. —*adj.* of or having to do with a trial in a court of law: *trial testimony.* [< Anglo-French < *trier* to try]

tri plet (trip′lit), *n.* **1** one of three children born at the same time to the same mother. **2** group of three.

tri pod (trī′pod), *n.* **1** a three-legged support for a camera, telescope, etc. **2** stool or other article having three legs. [< Latin < Greek *tripodos* < *tri-* three + *podos* foot]

ul ti mate (ul′tə mit), *adj.* **1** coming at the end; last possible; final: *He never stopped to consider the ultimate result of his actions.* **2** that is an extremity; beyond which there is nothing at all; extreme: *the ultimate limits of the universe.* —*n.* an ultimate point, result, fact, etc. [< Medieval Latin *ultimatum* < Latin *ultimus* last, superlative of root of *ultra* beyond] —**ul′ti mate ly,** *adv.*

u nan i mous (yü nan′ə məs), *adj.* **1** in complete accord or agreement; agreed: *They were unanimous in their wish to go home.* **2** characterized by or showing complete accord: *She was elected president of her class by a unanimous vote.* [< Latin *unanimus* < *unus* one + *animus* mind] —**u nan′i mous ly,** *adv.*

un doubt ed ly (un dou′tid lē), *adv.* beyond doubt; certainly.

u ni fy (yü′nə fī), *v.t., v.i.,* **-fied, -fy ing.** make or form into one; unite. —**u′ni fi′er,** *n.*

un ion (yü′nyən), *n.* **1** a uniting or a being united: *the union of hydrogen and oxygen in water.* **2** group of people, states, etc., united for some special purpose: *The ten provinces of Canada form a union.* **3** group of workers joined together to protect and promote their interests; labor union; trade union. **4** any of various devices for connecting parts of machinery or apparatus, especially a piece to join pipes or tubes together; coupling. [< Latin *unionem* < *unus* one]

u ni son (yü′nə sən, yü′nə zən), *n.* **1** harmonious combination or union; agreement: *They spoke in unison.* **2** identity in pitch of two or more sounds, tones, etc. [< Latin *unus* one + *sonus* sound]

a hat	i it	oi oil	ch child	ə = { a in about
ā age	ī ice	ou out	ng long	e in taken
ä far	o hot	u cup	sh she	i in pencil
e let	ō open	u̇ put	th thin	o in lemon
ē equal	ô order	ü rule	ᵺ then	u in circus
ėr term			zh measure	

u nit (yü′nit), *n*. **1** a single thing or person. **2** any group of things or persons considered as one: *The family is a social unit.* **3** a standard quantity or amount, used as a basis for measuring: *A foot is a unit of length; a pound is a unit of weight.*

u ni verse (yü′nə vėrs′), *n*. **1** the whole of existing things; everything there is; the cosmos. **2** the whole of reality. [< Latin *universum* whole, turned into one < *unus* one + *vertere* to turn]

u ni ver si ty (yü′nə vėr′sə tē), *n., pl.* **-ties.** institution of learning of the highest grade, usually including schools of law, medicine, teaching, business, etc., as well as (in the United States) a college of liberal arts and a graduate school. [See UNIVERSE.]

vac u um (vak′yü əm, vak′yüm), *n., pl.* **vac u ums** or **vac u a** —*n*. **1** an empty space without even air in it. **2** an enclosed space from which almost all air or other matter has been removed. —*v.t.* clean with a vacuum cleaner. [< Latin, neuter of *vacuus* empty]

ver dict (vėr′dikt), *n*. the decision of a jury: *The jury returned a verdict of "Not guilty."* [< Anglo-French *verdit* < Old French *ver* true + *dit* spoken]

vo cab u lar y (vō kab′yə ler′ē), *n., pl.* **-lar ies.** **1** stock of words used by a person, group of people, profession, etc.: *Reading will increase your vocabulary.* **2** collection or list of words, usually in alphabetical order, with their translations or meanings. [< Medieval Latin *vocabularius* < Latin *vocabulum*.]

vow el (vou′əl), *n*. **1** a voiced speech sound produced by not blocking the breath with the lips, teeth, or tongue. **2** letter that stands for such a sound. *A, e, i, o,* and *u* are vowels. *Y* is sometimes a vowel, as in *bicycle.* —*adj.* of or having to do with a vowel.

whole sale (hōl′sāl′), *n., adj.,* **-saled, -sal ing.** —*n*. sale of goods in large quantities at a time, usually to retailers rather than to consumers directly: *They buy at wholesale and sell at retail.* —*adj.* in large lots or quantities: *The wholesale price of this dress is $20; the retail price is $30.*

wind (wīnd), *v.,* **wound, wind ing.** —*v.i.* move this way and that; move in a crooked way; change direction; turn: *A brook winds through the woods.* —*v.t.* **1** fold, wrap, or place (about something): *wind a scarf around one's neck.* **2** make (some machine) go by turning some part of it: *wind a clock.*

wit ness (wit′nis), *n*. **1** person who saw something happen; spectator; eyewitness. **2** person who gives evidence or testifies under oath in a court of law. —*v.t.* be a witness of; see: *I witnessed the accident.*